NITRATE POLLUTION AND POLITICS

Nitrate Pollution and Politics

Great Britain, the Federal Republic of Germany and the Netherlands

JOBST CONRAD
European University Institute
Florence

Avebury Studies in Green Research

Aldershot · Brookfield USA · Hong Kong · Singapore · Sydney

Published by
Avebury
Gower Publishing Company Limited
Gower House
Croft Road
Aldershot
Hants GU11 3HR
England

Gower Publishing Company
Old Post Road
Brookfield
Vermont 05036
USA

ISBN 0 566 07147 9

Printed in Great Britain by
Athenaeum Press Ltd, Newcastle upon Tyne.

Contents

1 Introduction

Environmental problems of agriculture have received growing recognition in public debate and politics during about the last decade. Environmental pollution is no longer seen as a problem of industry and transportation only but as a potential negative effect of every social activity. So, the question how far environmental concerns can and do matter in agricultural policy is a relevant one.

The purpose of this book is to investigate the possibilities for and restrictions of increasing environmental concern in agricultural policy as revealed by the example of nitrate debate and politics. Therefore political processes in the field of agriculture and environment are analyzed with special reference to nitrate pollution of ground and drinking water, at the national, regional, local and EC level in order to come closer to answer to the question concerning the preconditions, determinants, possibilities and restrictions of an 'ecologicalization' of agricultural policy. The agriculture-environment debate which has developed strongly during the last decade in the countries studied clearly is an important part of the background to this book. Scientific, public and political concern about environmental aspects of agriculture has gained considerable prominance during the last years, but how to install environmental protection measures in agriculture to any great extent still remains a largely unresolved problem. Therefore, this book may contribute some hints to answering this question, though resting within the limitations set by any case study and by any policy analysis.

The book summarizes the debate and politics concerning the pollution of ground and drinking water by nitrate in three countries: Great Britain, the Federal Republic of Germany and the Netherlands. In comparing several countries, it is possible, on the one hand, to identify specific national characteristics of the nitrate debate, politics and policy and to speculate about the general features of the nitrate issue in these Western industrialized EC-countries on the other hand. In addition, some inferences may be drawn with respect to the agriculture-environment debate and policy structure in general and the role that nitrate pollution and politics are playing in this context.

These objectives can be achieved within a comparative monograph even though the relevant issues can be addressed only in summary. Consequently a rough survey of nitrate pollution and politics in these three countries is provided from which several conclusions concerning comparative aspects can be drawn. The book also refers to the main conclusions from the more detailed national case studies undertaken.

The description of the evolution of nitrate debate and politics is based on a larger research project 'Increasing Environmental Concern in Agricultural Policy' carried out under my responsibility at the Wissenschaftszentrum Berlin für Sozialforschung from 1983 to 1989. The general concept of the research project can be described as the analysis of nitrate policy and politics against the background of the agriculture-environment debate; the situation of agriculture and water supply; the structure of the nitrate problem; and the features of the nitrate debate. The policy cycle is studied at the national, regional and, in most countries, local level focussing on the 1970s and 1980s. The evolution of the policy game around nitrate is studied mainly with respect to the influence of both the key actors involved and the institutional structures shaping it. In view of the interests and strategies of the actors, the pattern of regulation and the severity and political importance of the nitrate problem, conclusions can be drawn about the substantive impacts of nitrate policy and about potential crucial policy measures necessary to increase environmental concern in agriculture as well as agricultural policy (see Conrad, 1984; Conrad and Knoepfel, 1984).

At a methodical level, the investigations are based mainly on expert interviews with relevant actors in the nitrate policy game and on the analysis of relevant literature. This involved official and unofficial documents, as well as secondary material from various newspapers, journals and the publications of interest groups up until around the end of 1987. This is important to realize because of more recent developments in nitrate politics in 1988, particularly for Great Britain. The political process has been studied in detail not only at the national and regional or local level, but also on the part of agriculture as well as water supply. The study is essentially an empirical-descriptive case study based on theoretical categories, drawn preferably from policy analysis literature. It does not attempt, however, to test specific theoretical explanations of the policy process. The implication of such an approach is that the reader has to rely on the validity of the evidence presented on two levels: First, it cannot control if the description of nitrate debate and politics is based on the appropriate selection of empirical data and material; however, this holds true for any empirical case study more or less. Second, it cannot excape a certain softness and arbitrariness of the interpretation of the empirical data because the chosen evaluation criteria and level of abstraction for the comparison of national nitrate politics and policies are not substantiated themselves. The comparison is organized according to analytical categories from policy analysis and does not primarily intend to supply the reader with a more hermeneutic understanding of the embedding of nitrate politics in the historically evolved pattern of national policy and politics. In sum, the comparative analysis of national nitrate politics and policies, as presented in this book, can claim plausibility but only partial scientific warranty.

The three countries analysed in this book have been selected for several reasons: First, nitrate pollution is dealt with politically in these countries; second, the research project was restricted to Western Europe; third, France and Switzerland have been investigated by other research teams with which we collaborated (see Knoepfel and Zimmermann, 1987; Larrue and Knoepfel, 1988), fourth, there was no manpower or research money available, respectively to include further interesting countries, such as Denmark, in the comparison. So, the three countries were selected for a combination of systematic and pragmatic reasons. Nevertheless, the results of the comparison support the conclusion that this selection was an interesting one for the study of the possibilities and restrictions to deal with nitrate pollution.

The structure of the book is as follows. First, in chapter 2, a very short description of the structure of the nitrate problem as currently perceived by scientists, is given. Then, the actual extent of nitrate pollution and the features of agriculture and water supply in Great Britain, the Federal Republic of Germany and the Netherlands are pointed out. In chapter 3, a brief history of the development of the nitrate debate and the arguments dominating within each country is presented. In chapter 4, the development of the major political approaches to regulation and the position of various political actors are described. Chapter 5 compares the three countries on a more descriptive level while more general and systematic comparative conclusions are drawn in chapter 6.

The results presented are especially based on empirical investigations by Michael Hill in particular, S. Aaranovitch, D. Baldock, H. Gitay and P. Wathern for England and Wales. G. Bennett and L. van der Kley did the work for the Netherlands; the contributions for West Germany were done by myself and by many other collaborators as follow: K. Bruckmeier, G. Gitschel, P. Hafenecker, G. Hünermann, P. Teherani-Krönner and W. Uka. The partial funding of the English case study by the Anglo-German Foundation is greatly acknowledged. Special thanks are owed to W. von Urff for commenting and judging the draft version of this book, to W. Uka for taking care of many of the figures presented in it, and to A. Zierer-Kuhnle (Wissenschaftlicher Text-Dienst, Berlin) for typing the manuscript.

2 Nitrate: facts and problems

The structure of the nitrate problem

When trying to understand and to improve the social treatment of a certain problem area it is essential in my viewpoint to comprehend the (scientific) nature of the problems addressed by the social regulatory efforts to a certain degree and not to remain on a policy level which completely abstracts from the substantive characteristics of the problems. Therefore, the reader is first provided with a short overview of the nature of the nitrate problem.

Figure 2.1 shows the general route of nitrate from the soil through ground and drinking water to its metabolic pathways in human beings. The principle sources of nitrate contamination of groundwater stem from:

- o nitrogen fertilizers used in agriculture to increase crop yields,
- o animal manure resulting from intensive animal husbandry,
- o mineralization of nitrogen from the N-pool (partly due to agricultural practices),
- o other (including natural) sources.

Whenever nitrogen fertilizer of one kind or another is applied, this is connected with an enhanced turnover in soil and increased washout of nitrate. How much of the nitrate not taken up by plants reaches groundwater aquifers, and after how long, depends on many variables such as the N_{min}-balance in the root zone, soil type, agricultural practices, type of crop, weather and the denitrification capacity of the soil. Table 2.1 provides an indication of the relationship between type of soil use and nitrate losses.

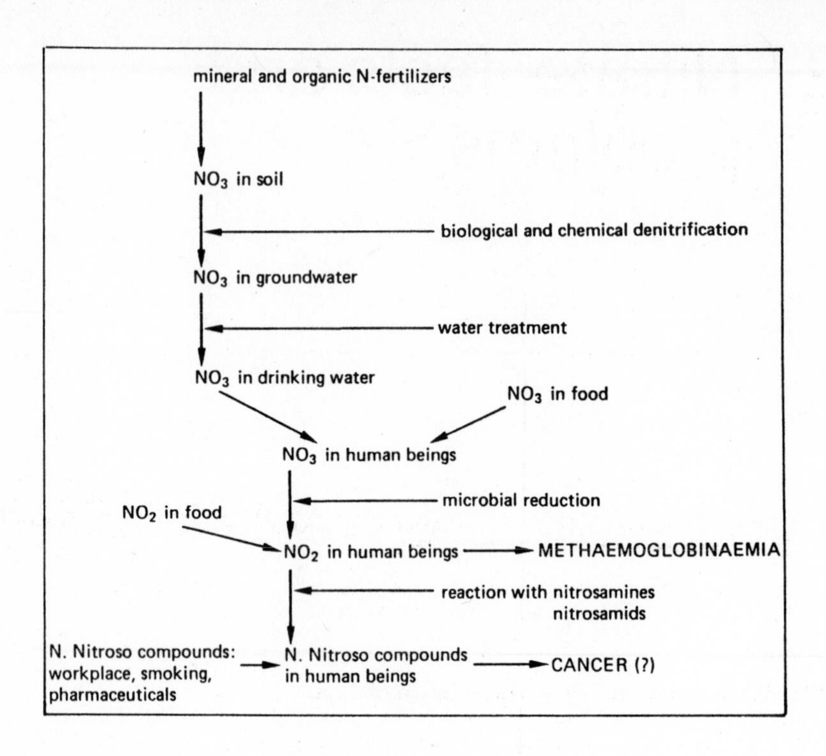

Figure 2.1 Nitrate pathway and metabolism

Table 2.1
Soil use and nitrate loss

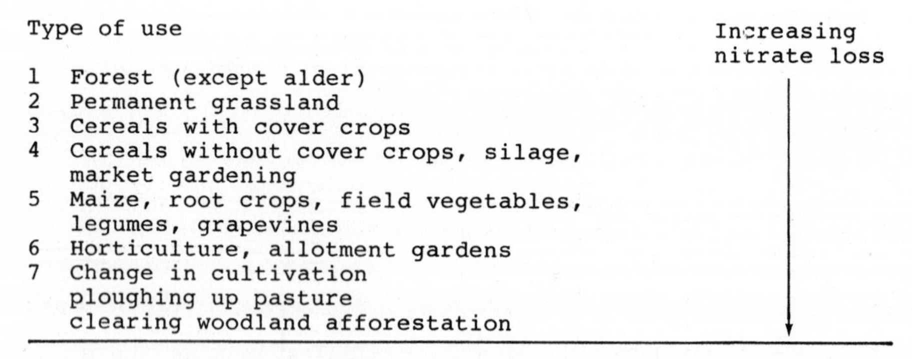

	Type of use	Increasing nitrate loss
1	Forest (except alder)	↓
2	Permanent grassland	
3	Cereals with cover crops	
4	Cereals without cover crops, silage, market gardening	
5	Maize, root crops, field vegetables, legumes, grapevines	
6	Horticulture, allotment gardens	
7	Change in cultivation ploughing up pasture clearing woodland afforestation	

Source: Vetter, H. (1985), 'Lösung des Nitratproblems - Was kann die Landwirtschaft tun?', *Agrar-Europe*, vol. 5, Sonderbeilage, p. 1.

Table 2.2
Utilized agricultural area (UAA), woods and forests

	United Kingdom			Federal Republic of Germany			Netherlands		
	1970	1980	1986	1970	1980	1986	1970	1980	1986
Arable land	7,109	6,925	6,952	7,535	7,264	7,244	824	827	876
Permanent meadow and pasture	11,637	11,907	11,583	5,500	4,754	4,537	1,326	1,160	1,108
Permanent crops	91	72	61	203	179	181	50	38	35
Total UAA	18,853	18,920	18,612	13,578	12,248	12,000	2,209	2,029	2,025
Woods and Forests	1,882	2,105	2,297	7,170	7,318	7,360	294	290	293
Area of the country	24,400	24,410	24,414	24,857	24,864	24,869	3,662	3,728	3,729

Source: BMELF, 1987; Kommission der Europäischen Gemeinschaften, 1983 ff.

Human beings ingest nitrate not only in drinking water but also in food, while the metabolic products of nitrate within humans can originate from other sources (cf. NAS, 1981). The two health problems which may be caused by nitrate ingestion are methaemoglobinaemia, especially dangerous for babies, and cancer, caused by N-nitroso compounds. Whereas the cause-effect relationship for methaemoglobinaemia is not controversial, there is, as yet, no definite proof that human metabolism transforms nitrite into carcinogenic N-nitroso compounds. Indeed, at present it is questionable whether doses of 200 or 300 mg NO_3 per day really are a relevant health hazard.

Higher concentrations of nitrate due to agriculture also have environmental impacts. They contribute to the eutrophication of surrounding and also more remote areas. In particular, the eutrophication of water bodies is known to shift the balance of an ecosystem towards plants with an affinity for nitrate. At present, however, the main reason for eutrophication of surface waters is phosphate. In some areas, large amounts of soluble nitrate can lead to a loss of denitrification capacity (Obermann, 1985) and higher permeability for heavy metals and pesticides.

At present, the main issue in all three countries is nitrate in ground and drinking water and its potential related health effects. High nitrate content in drinking water is observed especially in the regions of intense agricultural use. This problem can still be considered largely a local or, at most, a regional one in areas of intensive cultivation, high-density livestock farming, and wherever there are permeable strata above the water table (unsaturated zone). However, larger areas may be affected in the future, due to both the lag between increased nitrogen application and the rise in nitrate contamination of groundwater in many aquifers and the possible exhaustion of subterranean denitrification capacity (Obermann, 1984).

Before going into the national specifics of the interrelations between agriculture, water supply and nitrate pollution, Table 2.2 provides a general overview over the spatial role and structure of agriculture in all three countries.

Agriculture, water supply and nitrate pollution in Great Britain

In Great Britain, agriculture contributes about 1.8 per cent to the Gross National Product in the 1980s with regional variations between 1 and 7 per cent (Wathern and Baldock, 1987; Matthews and Trede, 1983). In economic terms, the most important agricultural products in the United Kingdom (UK) are milk, cereals and beef. There are important differences in both land quality and in physical characteristics which are reflected in the pattern of agriculture (see Figure 2.2).

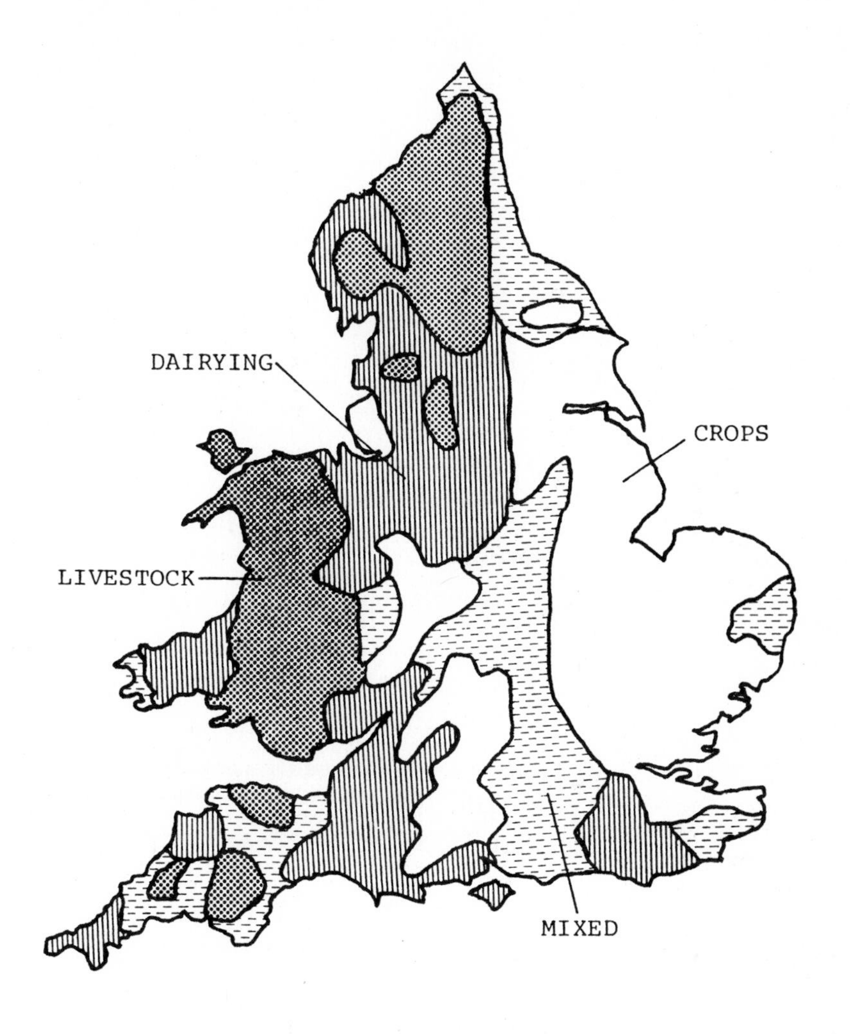

Figure 2.2 Regional variations in the pattern of agriculture in England and Wales

Source: Wathern and Baldock, 1987.

Most of the arable cropping takes place in the more fertile, drier and less hilly eastern part of the country. Altogether, agricultural land covers about 75 per cent of the UK. Compared to other EC-countries, the self-sufficiency of the UK in food production is still relatively low; however, it has risen from only about 30 per cent prior to outbreak of the Second World War to about 60 per cent today. With accession to the EC in 1972, prices rose considerably. In addition, the burden of support for agriculture shifted from the government, i.e. the tax payer through deficiency payments, to the consumer.

Given the 'advanced' status of most of British agriculture, questions of income policy are less important in Britain than in most other EC-member states. Certainly, there are farmers who survive only because of public subsidies. Animal husbandry in the less favoured areas (LFAs) in Scotland, Wales and Northern England, for instance, is profitable only because of the headage payments paid out according to the LFA directive EC 75/268.

A big increase in production has been achieved by raising yields per hectare and per animal. As in most other parts of Europe, these increases were achieved by the use of new varieties, the growing consumption of inorganic fertilizers and agrochemicals, improved agricultural research, advice and management, the employment of new technologies and extensive mechanization, investment in new buildings, farm structures and land improvement and the pursuit of greater specialization and mechanization. The application of nitrogenous fertilizers, which is of special importance for the nitrate problem in Great Britain, has grown from 35 kg N/ha in 1965 to 85 kg N/ha in 1985. However, these average figures disguise high rates of application on arable land.

Conservation and 'countryside issues' more generally have remained the most prominent environmental issues associated with agriculture in the UK. Attention has focussed particularly on certain types of designated areas, notably National Parks, Sites of Special Scientific Interest (SSSIs) and the new Environmentally Sensitive Areas (ESAs). The approach to conservation has been to rely as much as possible on the 'voluntary' approach and to avoid mandatory controls on farmers wherever possible.

Air and water pollution from agriculture, on average, tend to attract much less attention than wildlife and landscape issues, on average (Wathern and Baldock, 1987). The importance of nitrate pollution of both surface and groundwaters has become more apparent in recent years and it has become clear that a significant number of people rely on drinking water with a nitrate concentration above 50 mg/l. This applies especially to those living in intensive arable areas, such as East Anglia, where the main source of drinking water is groundwater.

The emergence of the nitrate issue onto the environmental agenda is occurring against the background of a changing debate about the relationship between agriculture and the environment. This change leaves British agriculture in a much more politically exposed position than before (Hill, 1988).

In 1986, the British government added a new clause to the Agriculture Bill whereby the Agriculture Ministers would be required to balance the needs of conservation, recreation and the rural economy against those of agriculture when taking decisions. This confirmed the political importance which the topic 'agriculture and environment' had attained during the previous six or seven years.

The agricultural policy community largely managed to remain a rather closed circle and to exclude 'new' actors, especially environmentalists, from the key bargaining and decision-making processes. Thus far, a quite effective strategy has been that of social demarcation and substantive appropriation which has kept responsibility and discretionary competence largely within the agricultural policy community, as is illustrated in the debates on agriculture and the environment.

It is significant that around 70 per cent of British drinking water is abstracted from surface rather than underground sources and that public sensitivity about groundwater has not been particularly marked in the past. There is a rising trend of water pollution problems associated with agriculture in the predominantly livestock-rearing western parts of the country, arising mainly from liquid manure (slurry) and silage effluent (Wathern and Baldock, 1987; Wathern 1988a).

There are ten public water authorities in England and Wales. Nitrate pollution problems are concentrated in three of them: Severn-Trent, Anglian and Thames. Southern, Wessex and Yorkshire areas also have some problems. These authorities face difficulties because it is the reduction of nitrate levels in groundwater which poses the greatest scientific and technical problems for efforts to reduce nitrate levels.

Therefore, what is central to the problem of nitrate concentrations in drinking water in Britain is the fact that intensive cultivation, applications of high levels of nitrogenous fertilizer and induced nitrate leaching through soil disturbance are concentrated in the south-eastern parts of the country where the underlying rocks are permeable and aquifers are essential water sources providing around 70 per cent of public water supplies. This does not mean that there are no concerns about nitrate concentrations in surface waters. However, with surface waters natural nitrate dispersal, dilution and denitrification occurs more readily, and can be enhanced, for example, by holding water in reservoirs. It should be added, however, that the most polluted surface waters occur where groundwater is a particularly important source of supply, thereby limiting the extent to which mixing provides a solution to the nitrate problem (Hill, 1988).

Some indication about the severity and regional distribution of nitrate pollution of drinking water can be gained by the data on derogations under the EC directive 778/80 on the grounds that the 50 mg/l standard for NO_3 cannot be reached in specific areas. These are given in Table 2.3 for 1985. From these data one can reasonably conclude that about 2 per cent of the population of *England* received drinking water with more than 50 mg/l NO_3 in the mid-1980s. Since predictions indicate a upward trend in nitrate pollution, presumably, if no preventive action is taken, a substantially greater number of derogations will be applied in due course. Meanwhile, however, the Department of Environment announced in 1988 that it will withdraw all the derogations for the nitrate parameter which it had previously sanctioned. The following predictions about groundwater are made:

> In regions of lowest rainfall (parts of Eastern and Central England) many groundwater nitrate concentrations are likely in the long-term to exceed 100 mg/l NO_3. In other parts of Britain, with the exception of the highest rainfall areas of the West, a large number of groundwater sources in unconfined aquifers are currently estimated as likely to reach equilibrium concentrations in the range 50 to 100 mg/l NO_3. (Department of Environment, 1986, p. 17)

In the same publication it is estimated that reduction to the 50 mg/l level would increase capital expenditure in the Anglian Water Region by 13 per cent over 20 years, while reduction to the 80 mg level would require an increase of 5 per cent; this would mean an additional expenditure of about £ 10 million per year to meet the 50 mg/l standard. The corresponding measures would be mainly blending, source replacement and denitrification technologies. Other aspects of nitrate pollution such as nitrates in foodstuffs and the potential loss of denitrification capacity of the soil, with its serious consequences for groundwater quality, have, as yet, received little public or official attention in the UK.

Table 2.3
Derogations for nitrate in drinking water in England 1985

Water Authority Area	Number of Supplies	Population Affected
Anglian	26	500,000
Severn Trent	24	372,000
Thames	1	48,000
Yorkshire	1	1,000
Total	52	921,000

Source: Department of the Environment, Memorandum, 1985.

Altogether, the knowledge and concern about nitrate pollution of ground and drinking water has grown considerably in the UK during the 1980s. The problem is essentially concentrated in the south-eastern parts of England where intense arable cropping, high rates of nitrogen fertilizer application, permeable rock and soil, and groundwater aquifers as essential drinking water sources coincide.

Agriculture, water supply and nitrate pollution in the Federal Republic of Germany

In the Federal Republic of Germany, the contribution of the agricultural sector to the Gross National Product has declined from 11 per cent in 1950 to 1.5 per cent in 1986. A closer view reveals that public subsidies for agriculture are of the same order of magnitude as agricultural gross value added, namely about DM 30 billion (Conrad and Uka, 1987). Agricultural production has increased strongly since 1945, from DM 25 billion in 1960 to DM 61 billion in 1986. The most important agricultural products are milk, cereals, beef and pork. Agricultural land covers somewhat less than 50 per cent of West Germany, meanwhile, self-sufficiency is around 100 per cent. The main features of agrostructural change can be seen in changes towards larger farms, fewer farmers, high capital intensity, intensification, specialization, and regional concentration.

The use of nitrogen fertilizer has risen from 20 kg N/ha in 1950 to 134 kg N/ha in 1987, stagnating since about 1980. Liquid animal manure from intense animal husbandry which is generally spread over the surrounding farmland amounts, on average, to 190 kg N/ha in those regions where animal husbandry plays a central role (Emsland and Süd-Oldenburg).

In the Federal Republic of Germany (FRG), part-time farming accounts for about 50 per cent of all farms; 40 per cent of part-time farmers gain more than 50 per cent of their income from activities outside agriculture. Notwithstanding, part-time farming, for which farm size is below average, is considered to be an integral part of German agriculture. It needs little political and financial backing and should help to preserve both the landscape and a certain population density in rural areas. Consolidation of farmland to improve agricultural production plays a considerable and ongoing role in the FRG. About one third of the utilized agricultural area (UAA) is under reconsolidation procedures at any given time. Agricultural structure is quite diverse in West Germany and has a North-South gradient.

Agricultural policy in the FRG is dominated by close relations between agricultural authorities and their farming clientel. Yet, the environmental problems of agriculture have received growing public recognition since the late 1970s (see SRU, 1985). Nitrate pollution of drinking water and conservation issues, particularly the loss of species, have been major issues in the agriculture-environment debate. Meanwhile pesticides seem to surpass nitrates in the public debate.

Drinking water supply in the FRG stems mainly from groundwater. Overall, excluding artificial recharge and bank filtration, it comprises 64 per cent of the supply, with regional variations of between 37 per cent and 100 per cent. Water supply is provided by about 6,300 water utilities, both large and small, which are mostly organized as private or public enterprises. Especially in rural areas of the northern parts of the FRG, many private wells supplying individual households with drinking water also still exist. The control of the water quality lies formally with the public water and health authorities at the regional and local level. In Great Britain water authorities combine the tasks of water supply and quality control for public water supply, while regulation of the quality of private water supply is a responsibility of District Councils through the environmental health authorities.

At present, about 6 per cent of the German drinking water boreholes contain water with nitrate concentrations above 50 mg/l. Average concentrations are rising continuously in regions of intensive agriculture by 1 - 2 mg/l anually. Therefore, investments for drilling deeper wells, for blending water, for connecting local supply to long distance water sources, and for installing denitrification technologies are being made and are expected to increase in the future. Finally, the agricultural advisory services give at least some attention to environmentally beneficial agricultural practices. The N_{min}-method to determine actual fertilizer requirements is increasingly applied. In some cases, even fertilization by special companies under government contract is seriously envisaged.

The main issue in the FRG is nitrate in ground and drinking water and its potential health effects. Nitrate in foodstuff and the environmental impacts of nitrate pollution play only a minor role in the nitrate debate. High nitrate levels in drinking water is observed especially in regions of intense agricultural use. Whereas in the northern parts of the FRG nitrate pollution is mainly associated with liquid animal manure from intense animal husbandry, it relates more to special crops like vineyards and vegetable growing in the south (see Figures 2.3 and 2.4).

Despite nitrate levels which are still rising in many areas used for drinking water supply, it is expected that water utilities will be able to meet the nitrate standard in the EC drinking water directive. In some areas, this may require a period of derogation so that the problem can be solved by corrective measures on the water or even the agricultural side. The costs for these measures will amount to around DM 1 billion per year for the FRG overall.

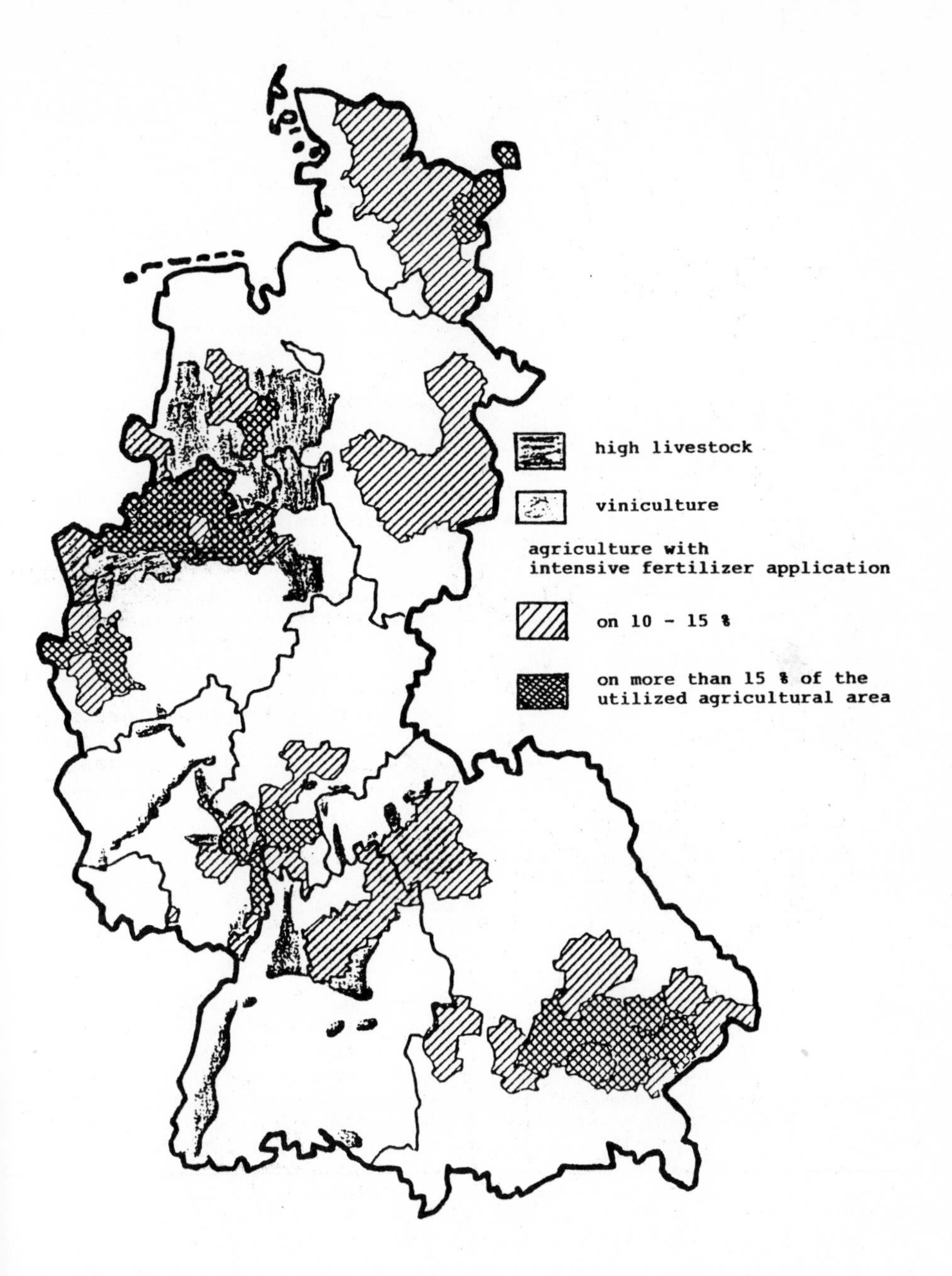

Figure 2.3 Agricultural intensity areas in West Germany

Source: Stiftung Warentest, 1988.

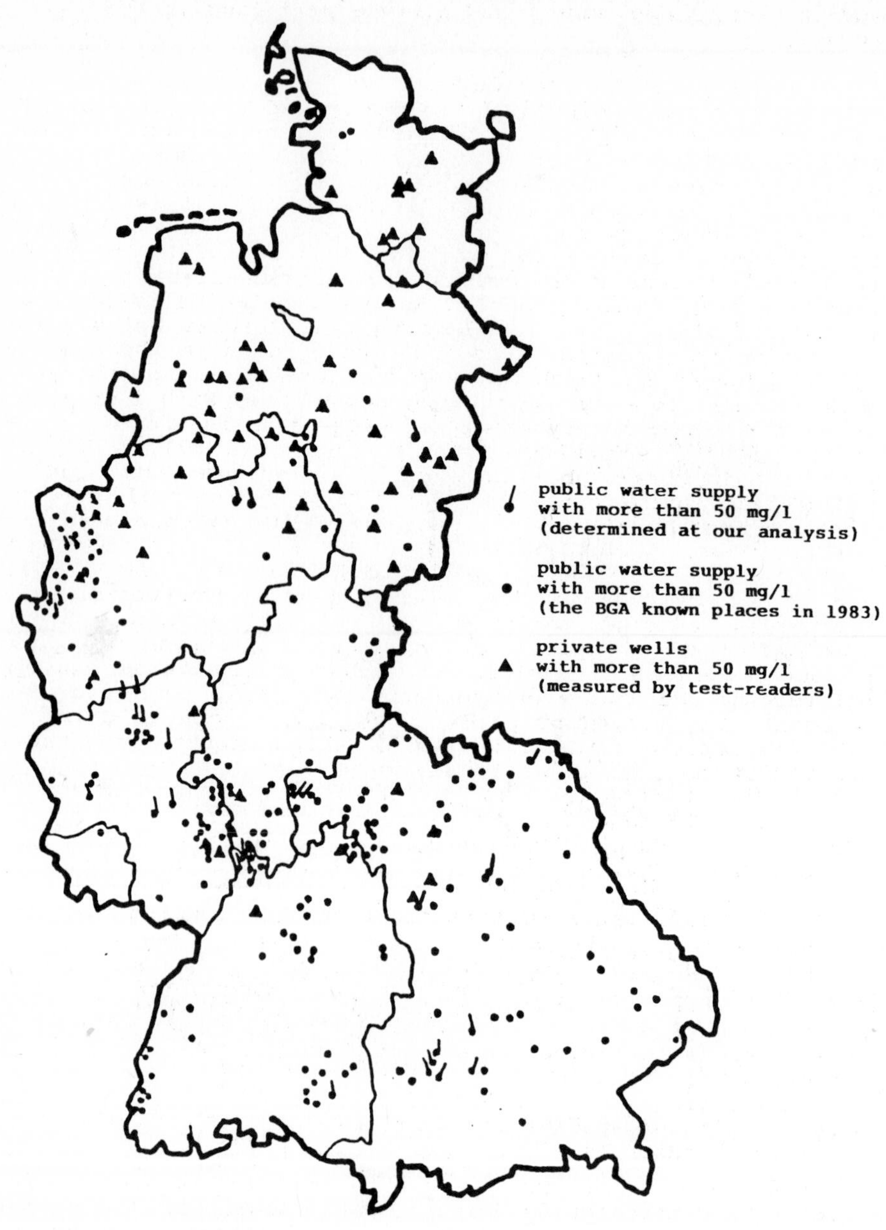

Figure 2.4 Excess nitrate concentration in drinking water in West Germany

Source: Stiftung Warentest, 1988.

Agriculture, water supply and nitrate pollution in the Netherlands

In the Netherlands, agriculture still plays an important role in the overall economy. Whereas the share of agriculture in the Gross National Product decreased from 10.5 per cent in 1960 to 4.2 per cent in 1985, one quarter of the country's exports stems from farming.[1] Dutch agriculture is renowned for its exceptional productivity. It is the most intensive in the world. Production figures have increased drastically since 1950 to hfl 31 billion in 1987. The shift to an agriculture dominated by a few specialized products, namely milk products, pork, beef and vegetables is one significant feature which has come to characterize Dutch farming during this period. The dominant changes in the production structure of Dutch agriculture involve increasing specialization, decrease in the number of farms with increasing dominance of the family farm, and an increasing role for industry in agricultural production (Bennett, 1987). Agricultural land covers about 54 per cent of the Netherlands. Self-sufficiency amounts to 25 per cent for cereals to 200 per cent for vegetables, and to more than 300 per cent for pork, chicken, butter and veal.

The Netherlands is not only a small country, it is also one of the most densely populated nations in the world. The achievement of such productivity levels is testimony to the high efficiency, capitalization, organization and expertise of Dutch farmers. Given the major role of agriculture in determining the nature of the Dutch landscape, and given the dominant role played by water in the Dutch economy which is also responsible for a good part of the country's importance in wildlife terms, it is hardly surprising that agriculture-environment conflicts have developed into major issues in recent years; indeed, they are now structural features of the country's economy and geography. The scale of the conflict is such that action is now regarded as a political imperative. Even the Minister of Agriculture himself has warned that further intensification of farming in the Netherlands has to be halted if the environment is not to be irreparably damaged. So, the environmental impacts of farming are profound and fall into six main categories:

- eutrophication
- heavy metal contamination
- groundwater pollution
- acidification
- destruction of species and habitats
- uniform landscapes.

Nitrate concentrations in groundwater are gradually increasing and threatening drinking water supplies. The geological structures most suitable for the abstraction of drinking water are the Pleistocene sand strata largely found in the east and south of the country. Unfortunately, groundwater beneath sandy soils is most susceptible to nitrate pollution from animal wastes, and yet it is in these areas that intensive livestock farming is concentrated (see Figures 2.5 and 2.6). Despite this huge surplus of animal wastes, considerable use is made of artificial fertilizers in the Netherlands where the application of nitrogen to agricultural soils has grown about fivefold since 1950 to stand at 249 kg N/ha in 1985.

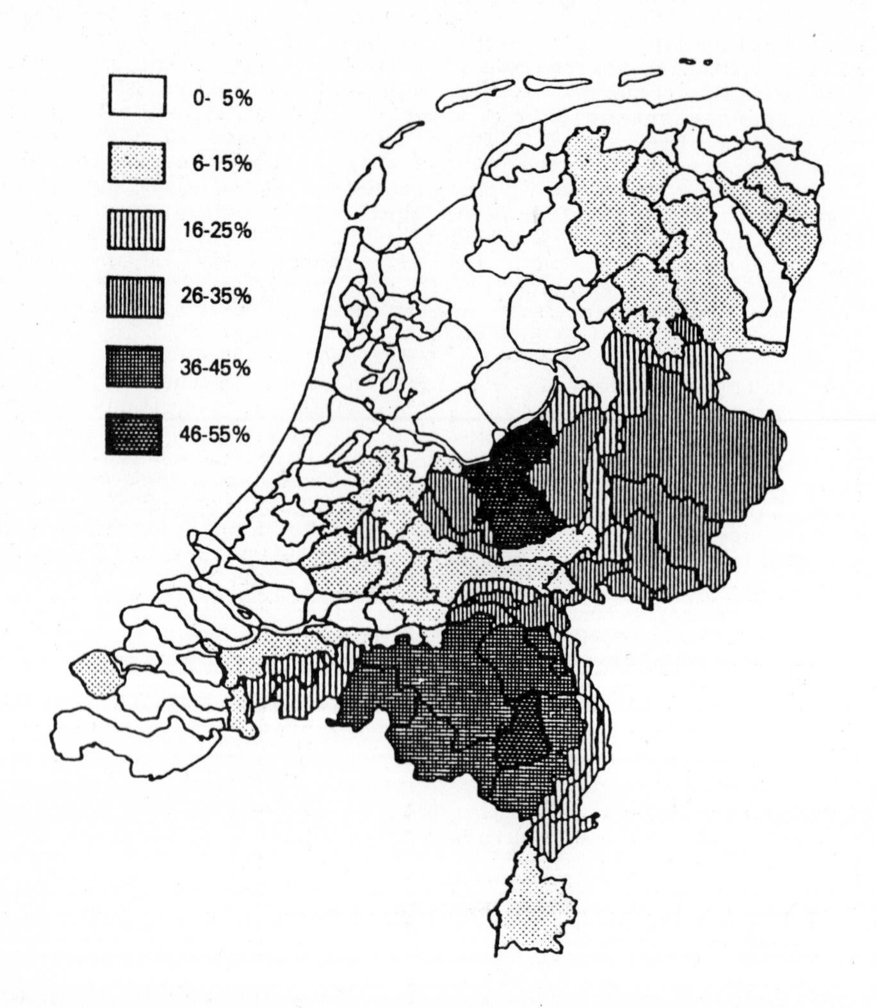

Figure 2.5 The share of intensive livestock farming in total agricultural activity in the Netherlands

Source: Bennett, 1986.

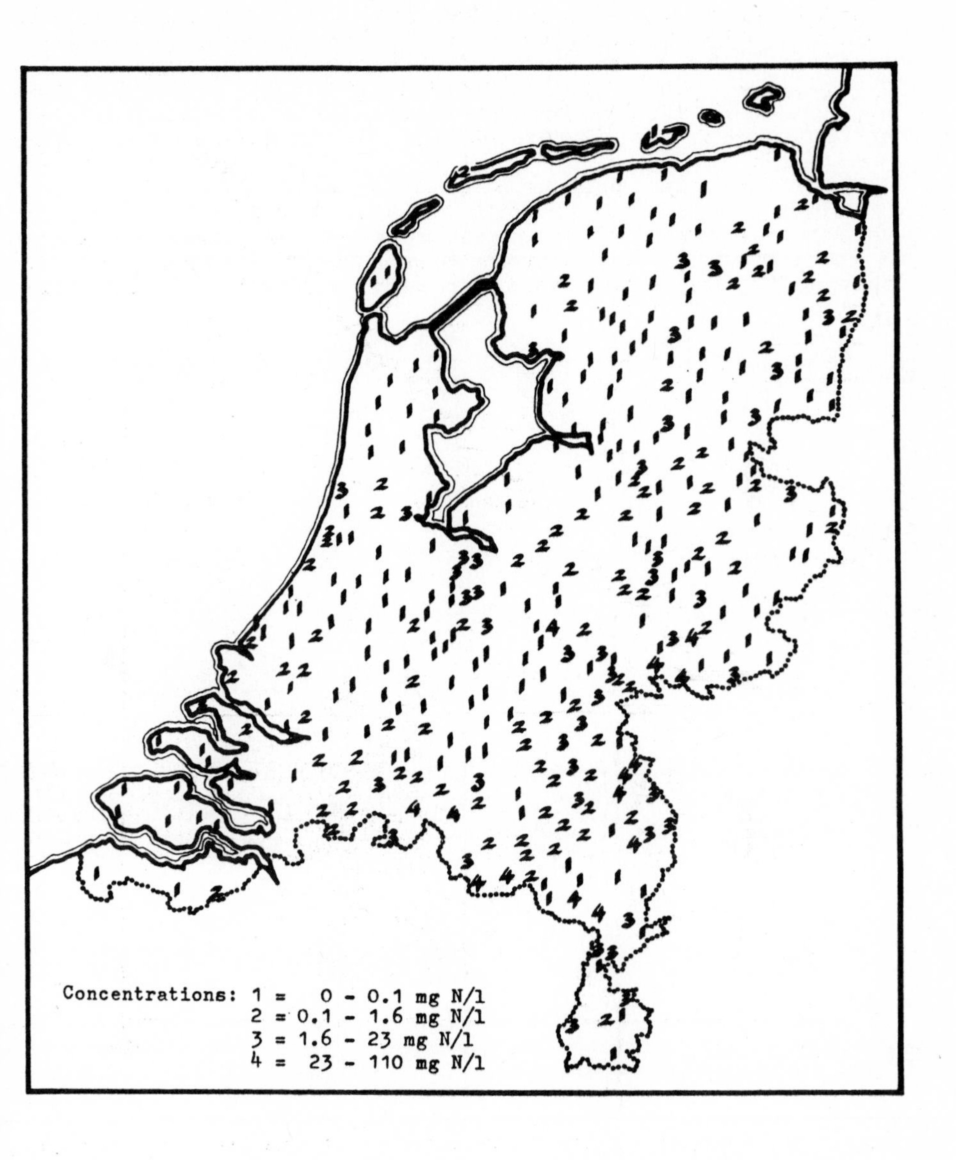

Figure 2.6 Nitrate concentrations at a depth of 10 m in the Netherlands

Source: van der Kley and Bennett, 1988.

The Dutch are renowned for their exceptional ability to control and utilize their huge water reservoirs. About two thirds of all drinking water is abstracted from groundwater supplies. Water is supplied by 88 water utilities in the Netherlands, most of them municipal water companies. Regional water authorities are responsible for the quality control of drinking water and for the development of water management plans.

Whereas nitrate pollution of groundwater is the focus of the nitrate debate, regard is also given to nitrate in vegetables, even to the extent that public standards exist. A related issue is the ammonia given off by dung which is thought to be an important contributory factor in the formation of acid rain.

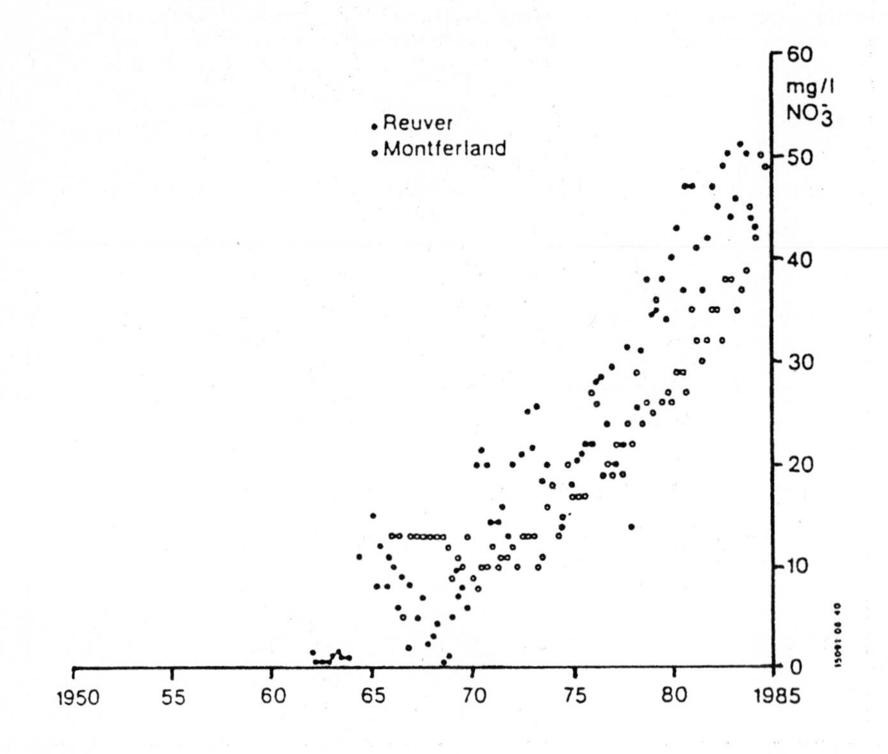

Figure 2.7 Trend in nitrate concentrations in the groundwater abstracted from water catchment areas situated in maize crop areas (Montferland en Reuver, Gelderland)

Source: van der Kley/Bennett 1988.

Obviously, nitrate pollution of groundwater is a central issue in the Dutch agriculture-environment debate. The main cause is the application of excessive amounts of animal wastes to the soil, especially in the south east where intensive livestock farming, sandy soils and large amounts of groundwater abstraction coincide. To make matters worse, these are the areas where, due to the type of soil (mainly sandy soil with no or very little organic matter), natural denitrification (the conversion of nitrates into nitrogen gas) is practically nil. It is not surprising, therefore, that in these areas nitrate concentrations in groundwater are rising to inadmissably high levels, thereby creating a considerable problem for the drinking water companies (see Figure 2.7). Altogether only about 0.8 per cent of drinking water has nitrate levels above 50 mg/l (DVGW, 1987). This low figure is a reflection of the expensive technical measures which have been adopted by the water utilities. Nitrate pollution is a serious threat to arable land, water reserves and to nature in general in the Netherlands.

Note

1. About three quarters of Dutch agricultural products are exported.

3 Development and structure of the nitrate debate

The nitrate debate in Great Britain

Although the link between methaemoglobinaemia and high levels of nitrate in drinking water has been known in Britain since World War II and a few cases of methaemoglobinaemia were reported around 1970, nitrate pollution did not surface as a matter of concern until the mid-1970s. The discussion and measurement of nitrate pollution remained essentially an affair between a few experts in government, water authorities and water research. The Royal Commission on Environmental Pollution commented on the nitrate problem in its seventh report in 1979, but saw no serious health risks for nitrate levels below 100 mg/l NO_3. The Royal Commission recommended that it would be more cost effective for water authorities to tackle the nitrate problem by way of blending or denitrification than to impose restrictions on the use of fertilizers (Royal Commission, 1979). This position has remained the official one up until today (1987), which was only very recently begun to change. Accordingly, the British delegation was the only one voicing strong reservations against lowering the nitrate standard in the EC drinking water directive 80/778 to 50 mg/l during its formulation in the 1970s (Kromarek, 1986). During the 1980s, the nitrate problem received more official and public recognition and was debated more intensely, for instance in Parliament, by the Department of Environment, the Ministry of Agriculture, Fishery and Food (MAFF), the fertilizer industry, the National Farmers Union (NFU), the water authorities, environmental groups, research institutes, several committees (e.g. the official Standing Technical Advisory Committee on Water Quality), and even in the environmental media. Despite this increasing prominence of the nitrate issue, it still remained only a minor part within the general agriculture-environment debate.

Apart from the focus on nitrate pollution of ground and drinking water, emphasis in the nitrate debate has been shifting continually. Currently, one may distinguish three views. One of these is to regard the extent of the problem of nitrate in drinking water to be exaggerated and, more specifically, to regard the EC level of 50 mg/l to be unnecessarily low. The second is to accept there is a problem, but to see it as one to be solved within the structure of the existing British pollution control system by regulating the polluting behaviour of farmers in specific local areas. The third and most radical view of the problem and its solution is to consider it necessary to have measures to curb, more generally, the use of nitrate fertilizers by all farmers, for example by a tax or a quota system (Hill, 1988).

The case for the first approach lies in its cheapness; the case against it, as made by the Friends of the Earth, is that it disregards potential health hazards. Further, it had the disadvantage that it brought Britain into conflict with the EC, because it could not justify the case for its derogations. According to Section of the EC drinking water directive derogations can be granted to cope with 'situations arising from the nature and structure of the ground'. Since such situations apply to much of southern Britain and several other parts of Europe, it could hardly be argued that this was an unusual natural formation. In addition, nitrate pollution by agriculture could not be described as 'natural'. Consequently, the British government was clearly open to challenge.

For the second approach, the question is to what extent British legislation, especially the Control of Pollution Act 1974 (COPA), provides the power to control nitrate pollution by agriculture. A water authority will find it difficult to attribute a specific nitrate pollution problem, particularly one in groundwater to which nitrates are slowly leached over a long period of time, to 'bad' practice by a specific farmer. The 'Code of Good Agricultural Practice', published by MAFF in 1985, does not actually restrict the use of inorganic or organic fertilizers. Farming activities which are carried out in accordance with the Code are considered 'good' practice, and as such are deemed to comply with COPA. The possible declaration of 'water protection zones' under the provisions of COPA, is securing careful consideration at present. While there appears to be an acceptance of the principle, practical details remain to be resolved. Here the crucial question is, would the polluter-pays principle be invoked and if so would it be implementend in such a way that a group of farmers whose land lay on certain geological systems be specifically disadvantaged? Alternatively, would they be compensated for the restriction upon their business activities and if so who would pay, government, the farming industry as a whole or water consumers?

The third view appears to offer a substantial contribution to the solution of the problem of nitrate pollution. It suffers from the unattractiveness of and opposition to the proposed directive measures.

In sum, the health risks of drinking water with a nitrate content above 50 mg/l, but below 100 mg/l, are not considered very serious in Britain. The causal role of farming practices, especially mineral fertilizer application, in nitrate pollution is, more or less, acknowledged. Yet, emphasis is laid on corrective measures which affect the water side, such as blending or denitrification. The view of most of the relevant actors is that the costs for remedial measures, especially those that affect farmers, such as water protection zones, shall be borne by the water authorities. The British nitrate debate has gained considerable momentum in the mid-1980s, but it remains to be seen what its actual impact on British nitrate policy will be in the long run.

The nitrate debate in the Federal Republic of Germany

The problem of methaemoglobinaemia was first discussed and investigated in the Federal Republic of Germany in the 1950s. Few cases of methaemoglobinaemia were actually observed. Apart from the German Research Society (DFG) research programme 'Nitrate-nitrite-nitrosomines' in the 1970s and even though a few water works had to close some wells with high nitrate concentrations, neither public debate nor politics were concerned with the nitrate problem in the early 1970s.

Only by the 1980s, however, was the nitrate issue able to raise general public and expert concern and debate. This led, among other things, to a polarization between agriculturalists on the one hand and water suppliers and health and environment oriented bodies on the other. The nitrate problem received periodic media coverage and was discussed in various scientific circles such as medicine, law, agronomy, soil science, hydrology, nutrition science, environmental sciences, and water technology. In addition, it became the focus of attention for lobbying groups concerned with agriculture, the fertilizer industry, water utilities, and environmentalists, as well as among the responsible public authorities. A considerable number of conferences, seminars, expert meetings and public hearing took place.

The various dimensions of the nitrate problem were perceived increasingly as parts of the same problem during the late 1970s when knowledge about these aspects grew. Polarization of the nitrate debate occurred mainly along the following four lines of conflict:

- o whether drinking water with nitrate content above 50 mg/l constitutes a health risk;
- o whether fertilization practices and distribution of liquid manure by farmers are the main cause of rising nitrate concentrations in groundwater;
- o whether preventive or corrective measures should be adopted to reduce nitrate contamination, for example, less fertilizer use and changes in agricultural practices, or blending and denitrification of drinking water;
- o whether the costs of remedial measures should be met by farmers (the 'polluter-pays principle'), the water supply companies and water consumers (the 'injured party-pays principle'), or by society at large (the 'taxpayer-pays principle').

If one reconstructs the development of the German nitrate debate along these four lines of conflict, the following picture emerges. The public and political debate, strongly influenced by the representatives of the various interest groups, follows the more scientific discussions with a certain time lag. Nitrate contamination of groundwater is seen as a mainly local or, at best, a regional problem at present, but as a potentially ubiquitous problem in the future due to the time lag between nitrogen inputs and increased nitrate washout into groundwater aquifers.

The health risks of drinking water with 50 to 100 mg/l NO_3 remain controversial and uncertain with the present status of medical research. In public, everyone tends to advocate avoiding a potential risk under such conditions of uncertainty. From a political viewpoint, however, implementation of the EC drinking water directive means that this question has lost its relevance. Now it is only consideration to meet the EC NO_3 standard irrespective of its health significance.

The causal role of agriculture in nitrate contamination of groundwater is contested less and less. However, the need to determine the influence of a number of different factors, such as cropping practice, soil type, weather conditions, denitrification capacity of the soil and groundwater aquifers, velocity of groundwater streams, well depth, and quantity of water extracted, is increasingly emphasized. As a consequence, the legally-relevant proof of establishing a definitive cause-effect relationship in any individual case remains a difficult task.

Most groups involved in the nitrate debate emphasize preventive measures. In reality, however, water treatment measures tend to dominate for two reasons. First, there are long time horizons in agricultural measures, as these are effective only after years or even decades. Secondly, water supply and quality measures can be more easily implemented and controlled.

Controversy is greatest about who should bear the costs and, here, agriculture tends to be the winner. Despite supreme court decisions, favouring the 'polluter-pays principle', the taxpayer and water consumer will still have to provide the necessary finances. This applies not only to water related, but also to agriculture related measures, as is evident from the amendment to the water management law and the 'water penny' (see chapter 4). This pattern of cost distribution reflects the politically strong position of agriculture and the exceptions granted to it, which can be observed in most countries. Altogether, it becomes clear that health and environment oriented lines of arguments are less successful the more genuine agricultural interests are affected.

In summary, the nitrate problem received considerable attention during the 1980s with the main emphasis on ground and drinking water contamination and on the risks of cancer from nitrosamines. The first peak of concern occurred around 1983. Since then, other issues related to the agriculture-environment interface, especially pesticides, have also gained prominence.

The nitrate debate in the Netherlands

Discussions on nitrate concentrations in drinking water in the Netherlands date back as far as the 1950s. The awareness of political actors concerning the potential health hazards of nitrate-contaminated drinking water (e.g. methaemoglobinaemia) led to the setting of a maximum nitrate concentration in drinking water of 100 mg/l. It was, however, only at the beginning of the 1970s that environmental groups raised the nitrate issue, in connection with the phosphate contamination problem of water, pointing to agriculture as the main culprit. Only in the 1980s did the nitrate issue become the focus of a broad debate. Factors initiating the debate were:

- o the introduction of the EC drinking water directive in 1980, which set a limit value of 50 mg/l NO_3;
- o growing concern over increasing nitrate concentrations in groundwater used for drinking water purposes and the subsequent closure of some water abstraction points in the province of Gelderland;
- o growing political and public awareness of agriculture, and especially intensive animal husbandry, as the primary cause of many environmental problems, including the nitrate problem.

The last two issues, in particular, received wide media coverage which led to a rise in public awareness of the nitrate problem. The key actors involved in the nitrate debate are the water supply companies, agriculturalists and environmentalists.

Whereas the application of excessive amounts of animal wastes by farmers is now widely accepted as the main cause for rising nitrate concentrations in ground and drinking water, there is still controversy about the consequent health risks. Despite the fact that real evidence for the health risk of nitrate is still lacking, public and political opinion in the Netherlands is that one should err on the cautious side and meet the EC NO_3 standard of 50 mg/l (van der Kley and Bennett, 1988).

Similarly, as in the Federal Republic of Germany, preventive measures on the side of agriculture is given priority in discussions, but in reality, however, water treatment measures still tend to be of greater importance. Similarly, farmers have been fighting for compensation for financial losses which result from restrictions on farming within water protection zones. However, the water utilities strongly oppose such a reversal of the 'polluter-pays principle'. This reversal is now established by law, the recent Ground Protection Act, under which farmers have the right to be compensated for their financial losses where their land is designated as a water protection area.

In retrospect, environmental groups were the first to attempt to raise public concern about nitrate contamination of groundwater during the early 1970s. Only after the introduction of the EC drinking water directive did the Association of Water Company Proprietors (VEWIN) - the umbrella organization of the drinking worker companies - recognize the extent and seriousness of the nitrate problem and become involved in the debate. Although pursuing the same interests as environmentalists, the VEWIN takes a more moderate point of view on the nitrate issue and the action which should be undertaken to combat the problem. The VEWIN is of the opinion that, whilst it will press for governmental actions to regulate nitrate input to the soil, it has no obligation to provide the government with solutions to the problem. It is willing, however, to take certain corrective measures. In this respect research on removing nitrate from groundwater has been carried out by the Dutch Waterworks' Testing and Research Institute (KIWA).

The Agriculture Board, the powerful consultative and cooperative organization for agriculture and horticulture in the Netherlands, is convinced that measures have to be taken to ensure that the present situation is not further aggrevated and has accepted the need for certain control measures to deal with the animal wastes problem. Yet, farmers themselves have been protesting loudly against the Minister of Agriculture's policy. They have, however, reluctantly accepted the new provisions, though arguing that any further measures taken against farmers have to provide for the resultant loss of income (van der Kley and Bennett, 1988).

During recent years the nitrate problem has obviously gained significance and attracted public concern in the Netherlands (cf. Der Spiegel No. 44, 1988, p. 270). Measures to deal with the problem have to and will be taken. It remains to be seen, however, how effective they will be, who is going to meet the costs, and whether the nitrate debate will continue to figure on the agenda of public discussion in the years to come.

4 Nitrate policy and politics

Nitrate politics in Great Britain

When tracing the evolution of politics around and policy about nitrate, one is able to identify little significant political action in the UK. In the 1970s, when the problem was perceived more thoroughly by some experts, certain committees published reports on the nitrate problem. Overall it was considered a minor and well manageable problem by the administrators confronted with it. The British delegation was the only one to raise concern about the possible costs of the reduced nitrate standard in the EC drinking water directive then in preparation. Nitrate control and regulation were not on the British policy agenda before the emergence of this directive in 1980. Until the mid-1980s, there has been no positive action to go beyond the exploration of ways of tackling the problem. Meanwhile the evolution of nitrate policy has gone beyond the mere establishment of an agenda with quite sophisticated discussions about the merits of denitrification versus protection zones in a number of local case studies. Mechanisms for securing action are there, in principle, in the responsibility of the water authorities to provide good quality water to consumers and in the control powers set out in section 31 of the Control of Pollution Act 1974. However, Britain has been criticized by the EC Directorate General for Environment (DG XI) for a lack of more explicit legislation to implement the drinking water directive (Hill, 1988).

Policy issues were hardly within the remit of the various committee reports until 1985, but these did make public the evidence on the upward trend of nitrates in water and on the links between fertilizer use and nitrate pollution. Since 1983, several parliamentary questions have also addressed the nitrate problem, pressing the government on the issue and on efforts to deal with it. In addition, ten groundwater sources were closed temporarily or permanently during 1983 because of high nitrate concentrations.

Subsequent British policy on nitrates was largely determined by government decisions during 1985. Thus, the issue is seen as one for water authority expenditure. Compliance with the directive would be achieved if pollution levels, as measures by a three month moving average, fell below the Maximum Admissable Concentration (MAC) of 50 mg/l. [1] Finally, derogations were made for certain supplies and Part II of COPA was put into operation with the agricultural interest protected by the Code of Good Agricultural Practice. However, after 1985 three developments threatened the *status quo*, namely water industry privatization, challenges in the interpretation of the MAC and derogations, and the rethinking of agricultural policy related to EC concern about over-production (Hill, 1988).

The plans of the conservative government to privatize the water industry have generated considerable political controversy and have been the centre of water related politics during the last ten years. There are three important features of privatization. First, it will force the government to take more direct responsibility for the regulatory powers which are at present delegated to the water authorities (appointed quasi-governmental bodies). Secondly, it will have to be much more specific about pollution standards, since private entrepreneurs will want to be able to predict prevention costs and enforcement cannot remain a matter of private agreement within the governmental machine. Thirdly, the costs of maintaining the present approach to pollution control will fall upon private profit-making bodies unless alternative provisions are made.

The Department of Environment also proposed simplifying the procedures under COPA in 1986, whereby Water Authorities can establish 'Water Source Protection Zones'. The new procedure would allow areas to be designated on a generic basis rather than individually and without the need for a local inquiry. This might encourage action by the Water Authorities, none of which had set up protection zones using the powers previously available under the 1974 Act. This inactivity in the past partly reflected fears that a water authority would fare badly at an inquiry and, furthermore, be required to undertake the difficult task of proving that practices on an individual farm were unambiguously responsible for specific pollution levels. As yet, no protection zones have been designated until 1987, but they are actively under consideration. The central issues in this debate remain whether farmers participation in protection zones will be voluntary or compulsory and whether compensation will be paid for loss of income.

In 1986, the environmental group 'Friends of the Earth' took the step of formally complaining to the European Commission about UK derogations. It challenged their legal basis and argued that nitrate should be classified as a toxic substance at concentrations of between 50 and 100 mg/l.

In August 1987, DG XI dispatched a formal letter to the British government requiring an explanation for six different points concerning implementation of the drinking water directive. Five of them concerned nitrate. In December 1987, the British government abandoned its approach to the determination of MAC. Then, in March 1988, it also withdrew derogations for areas where geological conditions would make compliance with the directive difficult. However, in doing so it did not specify how it would solve this regulatory problem. Thus, in 1988, the government seemed to be taking the whole issue more seriously, but still showed no sign of an explicit legislative response.

A further catalytic event in nitrate politics was the publication of the report 'Nitrate in Water' by the Department of Environment in 1986. It was, by and large, supportive of the *status quo* by, for example, questioning the health risks, arguing that water industry expenditure on blending and denitrification is, generally, a more cost effective approach than measures affecting agriculture, and pointing out the unfairness of the use of the 'polluter-pays principle' in this case. However, this report does explore the options on the agriculture side, suggesting, for example, that more careful use of fertilizer, and pleading for the designation of water protection zones. It is important to note, however, that the House of Commons Environment Committee (1987) argued that, in the light of more recent studies, the Department of Environment should ask the EC to review the nitrate standard.

Finally, the British determination to cut agricultural overproduction in the EC has had some impact on the environmental debate about restricing fertilizer use. Once it became apparent that one option for curbing of the level of agricultural production was to take land in some areas out of arable use or out of farming. Completely, it was not surprising that the idea of less intensive farming with less fertilizer use was raised as an alternative approach. In this lively debate, agriculturalists finally rejected the idea of a general limitation on nitrogen fertilizers, while the proposals of MAFF to cut agricultural production had no real bearing on the nitrate issue.

As a very centralized state, local regulation of the nitrate problem in the UK is of no significance for overall nitrate politics. Technically and organizationally, however, British policy regards the nitrate problem as very much an issue of local treatment. Up to now, costly measures have involved decisions by individual water authorities to blend, to close boreholes, to open new water supplies or to denitrify and, possibly in the future, to designate water protection zones where agricultural activity will be curbed. As a consequence, nitrate pollution was essentially dealt with by those water authorities affected by it below the surface of realizable public policy.

The regional case studies carried out (Aaranovitch 1988; Baldock, 1988; Wathern, 1988a, 1988b) indicate how the various water authorities are dealing with the nitrate problem. Depending on its local seriousness, incidental factors such as personal, communal and organizational influence play an important role, and how serious is their perception of the problem of nitrate pollution. In Wales and south-west England, the problem of surface waters by agricultural wastes plays at least some role. It is dealt with by the responsible water authorities, who also address farmers directly in some occasions, and not on a political level. Nitrate contamination of ground water supplies is an issue in London, Anglian and Yorkshire Water Authority areas. Significantly, it is an issue mainly restricted to the water authorities. Only in the London case investigated, the engagement of local citizen groups and politicians was of crucial importance. During the mid-1980s a change of the water authorities concerned could be observed towards a position which took the nitrate problem and the EC standard more seriously. It involved considerable investments in research and development of water related measures independently while the Department of the Environment remained still hesitant. Only recently, however, the agricultural side was tackled more directly on the regional level. With the evolving general view of the nitrates issue as a conflict between agriculture and water supply the realm of a pure water policy game about nitrate pollution has been left.

In sum, while there has been an acceptance of the existence of a nitrate problem, there has then been, until recently, a concensus that it is the *water industry's problem* as opposed to *agriculture's problem* although environmentalists, the water industry and the Department of Environment share this view less and less. This view has been sustainable simply because the issue has been the quality of drinking water and not nitrates in food or the deterioration in the environmental quality of lakes and rivers.

With this problem definition, solutions have concentrated upon the technologies available to the water industry rather than upon preventative measures falling upon agriculture. The predominant climate of opinion, however, is beginning to change.

In principle, the statutory framework for nitrate policy and regulation is already there in Great Britain. It only needs appropriate reinforcing regulations. The most stringent policy activity which seems likely at present involves active implementation of Section 31(5) of COPA which only would require executive action by the Secretary of State for the Environment. As the powers are already developed to the Minister, there would be no need for parliamentary involvement. The declaration of protection zones would, of course, involve the water authorities (or in future privatized water 'companies'). Even so, this COPA-oriented policy approach needs to be contrasted with the much more extensive political activity which would be involved if a statutory attempt to control overall nitrate use were made. The Department of the Environment would require the much more active support of the Ministry of Agriculture and legislation would be necessary. Without the legislation debate, associated with much of the politics of nitrate pollution control is essentially private and hidden from even parliamentary surveillance. In 1986, while the Nitrate Coordinating Committee was still deliberating, a junior Minister at MAFF, ruled out nitrate regulation measures which would require MAFF support.

Much of the controversy goes on between MAFF and the Department of Environment, and any far reaching preventive measures are likely to be curbed by MAFF. Environmentalists played some role in nitrate politics in the 1980s, but their impact on nitrate policy was, at best, an indirect one namely stirring up public debate.

Altogether, the health and environmental problems of nitrate pollution have been taken more serious in Great Britain since the mid-1980s. However, they are still considered to be 'not proven' and only minor issues by the majority of the actors involved. There is no explicit British nitrate policy, beyond an acceptance of the need to comply with the 50 mg/l MAC and it remains to be seen what type of technico-administrative regulations will be implemented in the future, following the decisions of implementing the EC drinking water directive and the advisory leaflet sent to all farmers by MAFF.

Nitrate politics in the Federal Republic of Germany

In the 1950s and 1960s, when nitrate was not a political issue, fundamental decisions were made which not only contributed to the generation of the nitrate problem but also predetermined its political treatment. These decisions were related to developments in: agricultural, water and regional policy; in the pattern of political influence and decision-making in the field of environmental and health policy; activities directly related to nitrate (particularly advice on fertilizer application); recognition of the health risks of nitrate. The orientation towards agricultural expansion and yield increases, the neglect of the environmental dimension of agricultural production, the expansion of water supply, the neglect of environmental aspects in regional planning, and the advice to apply high amounts of nitrogen fertilizer (well followed by farmers) all contributed to the subsequent evolution of the nitrate problem.

The nitrate problem gained public significance and political relevance because of the chance occurrence of four main influential factors:

- o In recent years, a continuous increase in nitrate concentrations in water boreholes, mainly in areas of intensive agriculture, was observed by water utilities which led to well closure in quite a number of cases.
- o Such local events initiated local public debate in some communes which was generalized by the media to read, for example, 'agriculture a polluter of groundwater' or 'nitrate a time bomb in other regions too'.
- o Only implementation of the EC drinking water directive of 1980 generated any political necessity for action. At the same time, the conflict of interests between agriculture and water supply became more apparent.
- o The nitrate issue must be seen as part of a growing general agriculture-environment debate which not only provides a broader perspective and interpretative framework for the analysis of specific cases and issues but also facilitates their public recognition.

In the 1970s, the nitrate problem essentially remained within the realm of scientific research and expert debate. Thus, in the drafting process of the EC drinking water directive the nitrate parameter was hardly an issue. Even in the 1980s, when a public nitrate debate certainly exists, one cannot speak of a specific nitrate policy in the Federal Republic of Germany.

Within the context of the nitrate debate, different - sometimes coordinated - approaches towards the treatment and regulation of the nitrate problem can be observed. Many individual measures such as certain activities of the agricultural advisory services, including the N_{min}-method, water company decisions on investments and specific research activities, remain below the regulatory threshold at present. However, several relevant regulatory developments, which form the core of a German 'nitrate policy', can be distinguished:

- o the Drinking Water Ordinance, the Trinkwasserverordnung (TVO), was revised to its final form in 1986 to comply with the EC MAC;
- o the West German Water Management Law, the *Wasserhaushaltsgesetz* (WHG), was amended in January 1987 to include fertilizer limitations in protection zones and to provide for compensating farmers;
- o the state of Lower Saxony introduced a liquid manure decree in 1983;
- o the state of North Rhine-Westphalia introduced a liquid manure order in 1984;
- o a joint working group of the water utilities and water authorities (DVGW/LAWA), in collaboration with co-opted agricultural representatives, attempted to prepare new recommendations for water protection zones with special consideration given to nitrate. These have not come yet into effect;
- o research projects on nitrate questions have mushroomed during the last few years;

- the concept of a tax on nitrogen fertilizer was discussed but rejected by the agricultural ministry;
- the state government of Baden-Württemberg decided to introduce the so-called water penny in 1987, to be paid by water consumers to partly compensate farmers for eventual loss of income due to restrictions on fertilizer use within protection zones;
- efforts by the advisory services to encourage farmers to use less fertilizers were supported by official policy declarations.

The West German Drinking Water Ordinance 1976 had to be revised according to conform with the EC drinking water directive. Under the terms of the directive, the 50 mg/l standard would have had to be incorporated into national law within two years and actually implemented within five years. In fact, these requirements were not fulfilled by the German government, as the TVO was not revised until 1986. It became clear that derogations from the nitrate standard would be necessary for a substantial number of drinking water sources. Knowledge about the overall number of derogations issued by the responsible local authorities is fragmentary only because of the rather decentralized structure of water regulation and control in West-Germany, as compared to the UK. The resistance of the German health ministry to produce such a list and other information has led recently to some conflicts between the ministry and the DG XI of the European Commission. Probably the most important impact of the EC directive was a trigger effect, initiating public and private efforts to reduce nitrate concentrations in expectation of the revised TVO.

The 5th Amendment to the Water Management Law intended further improvements in water protection. With regard to agriculture, there were two significant changes between the earlier, more restrictive drafts of this legislation proposed by the Federal Ministry of the Interior in 1984 and the final version passed in 1986. The possibility of limiting environmentally hazardous agricultural practices, including fertilization, was restricted to water protection zones (§ 19) as opposed to general regulatory authorization (§ 3). Compensation payments to farmers for restrictions on agricultural practices in water protection zones were made obligatory, despite the dissenting votes of almost all the experts and lobbies consulted. This appears to have been a great success for the agricultural lobby.

The question of who should pay also blocked the development of recommendations for water protection zones by the 'Nitrate' *ad hoc* working group of the DVGW/LAWA 'Water Protection Zones' Committee which was constituted in 1983. The agriculturalists invited to participate in this *ad hoc* group insisted on compensation payments. The new leaflet W 104, intended to make recommendations for agricultural practices in water protection zones according to the prevailing soil and hydrogeological conditions, still exists only in draft after more than three years of discussion. Similarly, the long-overdue code of good agricultural practice has been the subject of controversial debate in various committees. It now appears that the German courts may have the final say over the issue of compensation for farmers in water protection zones.

Parallel to the WHG amendment, the introduction of a water penny in Baden-Württemberg was intensely debated. The water penny represents one way of making the compensatory payments required under the WHG operational. It would be paid by the water utilities who, in turn, would pass it on to the consumers. It is still an open question in 1988 as to whether the courts will decide against the admissibility of the water penny. Although it is still too early to judge the environmental benefit of the water penny regulation it appears that more stringent requirements and control of farming in water protection zones are necessary.

In 1985 the German Council of Environmental Advisers (*Rat von Sachverständigen für Umweltfragen*) delivered a special report on agriculture and the environment, in which, among other things, it proposed to raise a tax of DM 1.50/kg N on nitrogen fertilizer. This tax would be redistributed to farmers according to farm size so that only farmers with high N-fertilizer dosages would suffer from the tax. The objective, in combination with other nitrate-related proposals, was to cut at least peak fertilizer rates in order to reduce nitrate washout into groundwater. This tax proposal was strongly opposed by the agricultural lobby and by the ministry, and is not considered a serious approach to nitrate regulation by the relevant decision-making bodies. Only recently, the idea of a tax on fertilizer gained significance in public debate again.

Nitrate washout from liquid animal manure spread on the land in regions of intense animal husbandry is one of the most important problems. Animal manure is mainly a waste product of large-scale animal farms, which farmers want to dispose of as easily as possible. In addition, intense animal husbandry is often found in regions with less-fertile, sandy soils where nitrate percolates quickly to the groundwater. Therefore, the governments of Lower Saxony and North Rhine-Westphalia (*Länder* with considerable intensive animal husbandry) issued similar liquid manure ordinances in 1983 and 1984 respectively. The ordinances are based on the Federal Waste Disposal Act (AbfG) and restrict the application of liquid animal manure which must not be spread during the winter nor at more than 240 kg N/ha/year. In both cases, the agricultural lobby has not been able to prevent the adoption of these regulations, but it has succeeded in weakening its standards (see Conrad and Teherani-Krönner, 1989; Teherani-Krönner, 1985, 1987, 1988a). The main impact of these liquid manure ordinances has probably been less on the reduction of nitrate washout and more on the generation of increased environmental awareness amongst farmers. They have not been without effect for the legislation has facilitated the availability of subsidies for farmers willing to build liquid animal manure storage tanks and may yet also prepare the ground for further environmental regulation of agriculture in the future.

It was mainly public concern and debate which created a certain pressure to tackle the nitrate problem. The impact of public debate on finding a substantive and lasting solution to it, however, has been limited. The states play a central role in West German nitrate policy. This can be explained by, among others, the following reasons:

- o The legislative power for water regulation is primarily with the *Länder*.
- o Attempts to introduce a federal liquid manure ordinance failed.
- o The structure of agricultural production differs between states in the north and south leading to different agricultural interests.
- o Genuine environmental and water protection policy measures at a local level rarely develop in rural areas without pressure and prescriptions 'from above'.

In Table 4.1, the main features of nitrate policy at the state level are summarized for each of the larger *Länder*.

Without claiming representativeness, some conclusions can be drawn from the 13 case studies on the local treatment of the nitrate problem carried out within the framework of German nitrate policy project mentioned above. [2] Local nitrate controversies played a significant role, reflecting the fact that policy programmes have to be implemented in the real world mostly at the local level if they are to have substantive impacts. Summarizing the results of the local case studies, the following points appear worth mentioning:

1. In the last resort, the nitrate problem is always solved primarily by water-related measures, e.g. by the construction of new main supply systems, by drilling new wells and by blending water.
2. Measures related to agriculture are increasingly pursued. Their immediate effectiveness, however, is limited and hard to control. Most restrictions on agricultural practices are accompanied by compensation payments which are accepted by most actors.
3. Higher level programmes concerned with agricultural environmental policy, such as the liquid manure ordinances, strongly influence local nitrate policy, but do not question the priority of water-related problem solutions.
4. In the northern part of West Germany, local and regional excess liquid animal manure and a large number of private wells, frequently with high nitrate concentrations, characterize the problem. In the middle and southern part, nitrate washout from high doses of mineral fertilizer in areas of special crops (viticulture, fruit, legumes, etc.) and increased nitrate content in public wells are more characteristic.

Table 4.1
Main features of nitrate policy till 1987 at the state level

state	development of a substantive agricultural environmental policy	separate ministry of environment since	nitrate related policy programs	nature and size of local problems	political relevance of the nitrate problem (+, o, -; till end of 1987)
Schleswig-Holstein	low till now, probably more in the future	no	liquid manure guideline, experiment "Isle of Föhr", nitrate register of the chamber of agriculture, measuring system of groundwater quality, extensification programs etc.	distribution of liquid animal manure, many private wells, potentially affected the whole Geest ridge (~ 50% of the state)	- (o)
Lower Saxony	low till now, a lot of symbolic policy	1986	liquid manure directive, measuring system of groundwater quality, renewal of lake Dümmer, subsidization of liquid manure storage tanks, treatment and banks extensification programs etc., water resources planning, advice on fertilization	distribution of liquid animal manure, many private wells, regional nitrate problem (district of Weser-Ems)	o
North Rhine-Westphalia	medium, a lot of symbolic policy	no	liquid manure order, water protection area planning, subsidization of liquid manure storage tanks and treatment and of nitrate research, advice on fertilization, measuring system of groundwater quality, extensification programs, etc.	distribution of liquid animal manure, vegetable growing (transformation of grassland into arable land), private wells, potentially affected areas: Köln-Aachener-Bucht, Münsterland with local variations (ca. 50% of the state)	+

Hessia	low till now, coupling of social and environmental objectives in policy (grassland programs)	1985	grassland and extensification programs, measuring system of groundwater quality, advice on fertilization, ecology consultants, promotion of organic farming, subsidization of liquid manure storage tanks	special crops (e.g., grapevine, vegetables, fruits), only very local problems	-
Rhineland-Palatinate	low till now, symbolic policy	1985	measuring system of groundwater quality	special crops, especially viticulture; regional problem: river valleys, Rhenish Hessia Rhenish Palatinate	o
Baden-Württemberg	medium, more than symbolic policy	1987	water penny and ecology program, water protection area planning, promotion of nitrate research (more than any other state), measuring system of groundwater quality, advice on fertilization, including demonstration projects	special crops; regional problem: river valleys, upper Rhine valley plane, Swabian Alb (ca. 20% of the state)	+
Bavaria	low to medium, coupling of social and environmental objectives in policy	1971	measuring system of groundwater quality, subsidization of liquid manure storage tanks and nitrate research, extensification programs etc., advice on fertilization, liquid manure program and special regulation for water protection areas (from 1988 onwards)	distribution of liquid animal manure, special crops, both depending on soil type and conditions; local and regional problems: area around Munich, Lechfeld, Danube valley plane, locally in Franken, valleys of the Main and affluent creeks	o

5. There is no strong correlation between the severity of the problem (that is nitrate concentration above the standard), problem perception (public debate) and problem solution (taking substantive measures). In those situations where local public controversy arose, the major decisions concerning specific solutions had, in most cases, already been made.
6. The agricultural side was rarely involved in these controversies. The contrary was true for the local water utilities and environmental groups. The situation with respect to the involvement of the health office (*Gesundheitsamt*), the communal administration and local politicians in the public debate is less clear. In some instances, they were involved, but there was no clear pattern.
7. The main conflict usually concerns the health risks of drinking water which is (occasionally) above the old or the new nitrate standard. Thus, water utilities and water authorities have been ranged against environmental groups and the Green Party. The causal role of agriculture is only mentioned in general terms and is not the point at issue. This fact may also reflect the absence of farmers in most local controversies.
8. Public debate has been triggered by a number of causes including reports in the media, water utilities, local government and environmentalists. These variations in cause have had no significant influence on the future development or the chosen problem solutions in a particular case.
9. In most cases, the local press was the prime forum for controversy.
10. Regulations had greater input upon water utilities than on farmers. The rigorous standards of the TVO resulted in a strong impact of federal and state nitrate policy upon water utilities throughout Germany. In contrast, farmers were largely inaffected except in the two German states where only liquid manure ordinances played an important role.
11. The understanding and acceptance of the often precarious financial situation of farmers have probably been responsible for the fact that they have had to make only limited concessions. Local power relations do not seem to have influenced the chosen problem solution which has always been a water-related one. Only in the city of Augsburg did the weak position of agriculture contribute to a local nitrate policy which rapidly put some restrictions on farmers within the city limits.
12. Local nitrate controversies developed in most cases parallel to or after the evolution of nitrate related activities and programmes at the federal and state level. They were more or less sparked off from the outside. In the few exceptional cases of early local controversy, the issue had some impact on the problem perception and programme development at 'higher' levels of nitrate policy.

13. Analysis of local constellations do not allow unequivocal conclusions concerning regulatory styles. There exist cases of 'silent' and 'loud', of 'procedural' and 'power' and of 'non-activity' solutions [3], to the nitrate problem on the local level (see Bruckmeier, 1987a).

Concerning nitrate policy, the form of defining the problem is probably related to a number of factors. It reflects the strong (direct and indirect) influence of science, the confrontation of agriculture and the water industry, the mixing of factual and financial arguments, the existence of problem solutions within the usual routines of politics and the exemption of the core of agricultural policy from the discussion. Also, the dominance of the nitrate contamination of drinking water issue tends to lead to some neglect of other, perhaps more pressing, environmental problems concerning agricultural policy for a time.

In changing the rules of the nitrate policy game at the meta level, the following trends of development can be observed:

1. External restrictions on agricultural practices for environmental reasons appear to be increasingly acceptable policy measures.
2. At the same time, farmers increasingly succeed - within certain limits - in fixing the legal right to receive compensation for simply avoiding environmentally hazardous agricultural practices and, in effect, open up a new source of agricultural subsidies.
3. There is intense debate about and a gradual shift in the interpretation of the polluter-pays principle in agriculture.
4. The limited participation of environmentalists and the public in the policy game around nitrate is probably mainly due to their generally increasing consideration in environmental policy-making and less due to special strategies of the main actors involved.
5. The strategy of establishing a general priority for groundwater protection for (future) drinking water use over other objectives of land use has not yet been successful despite having been followed by the water authorities and utilities since about 1983.
6. A gradual opening of agriculture, though less of agricultural policy, to environmental concerns can be observed since the 1980s. However, one cannot yet speak of an efficient agricultural environmental policy.

The pattern of nitrate regulation in West Germany can be characterized as gradually evolving, more or less segmented regulation of drinking water. These regulations slowly expand on the basis of applying legal norms and standards from health and water policy to agriculture. In general, the impacts of agricultural policy and economics are excluded in their formulation with the exception of compensation payments to farmers. At a political level the formal implementation of such regulations appears to be more relevant than their actual effectiveness.

The most important deficiencies in nitrate regulation refer to its cause- orientation, its effectiveness and its efficiency. Juridical and administrative practicability, political viability and societal conformity are fulfilled much better.

Nitrate politics in the Netherlands

As in England and West Germany, the nitrate problem in the Netherlands largely remained a topic for a small number of experts until the 1970s. Then, however, the Foundation of Nature and Environment, an environmental pressure group, made the link between intensive livestock farming and nitrate pollution and voiced protest against this situation in the early 1970s, but hardly anybody listened to these protests. This was probably because nobody foresaw the enormous increase in numbers of livestock in later years, encouraged by EC agricultural policy, which would lead to continuously rising nitrate levels in groundwater. The water supply companies failed to comprehend the danger of slowly rising nitrate concentrations in drinking water until the introduction of the EC drinking water directive in 1980. Then, the VEWIN realized that the nitrate problem was real and dangerous and initiated the nitrate debate. The Dutch government accepted the EC directive. The VEWIN subsequently urged the government to take measures in order to prevent nitrate washout to the groundwater in water catchment areas. However, the VEWIN was of the opinion that it is not their task to provide the government with ready-made solutions to this problem. The Foundation for Nature and Environment, on the other hand, went much further in this respect. It has continued to work on the developing alternative (environmentally more compatible) agricultural methods. Differences in working methods explain the lack of cooperation between these actors, who share more or less the same interests with regard to the nitrate problem.

Why did the nitrate pollution issue suddenly receive top priority on the political agenda? This can be explained best by the fact that the political will to solve the nitrate problem coincided with and was, therefore, invigorated by the political aim of finding solutions to the animal wastes problem and of achieving an environmentally more compatible agriculture. It should be noted that, at this time, other environmental problems partly caused by agriculture, such as the 'acid rain', phosphate and pesticides problems, were also high on the political agenda in the 1980s. Furthermore, escalating EC financial and intervention storage problems and the resulting measures announced by the EC to curtail the production of agricultural goods have certainly played a major role in this respect. Another measure which might have influenced the Dutch government in their choice of policy strategy was the outcome of the public discussion at that time. This public discussion was heavily influenced by the media, which were extensively used mainly by the environmental groups.

Still it was no simple task to confront the agricultural sector with negative measures. As expected, farmers opposed all measures, especially if compensation for loss of income was not provided. Since they are the most powerful lobbying group involved in the debate, farmers have a lot of influence on the realization of nitrate policy. Moreover, the Dutch economy depends heavily on agricultural export. This also explains why it has taken so long for the nitrate problem to be recognized politically as a serious problem and for measures to be taken to solve the problem.

There is at yet no specific nitrate policy in the Netherlands. Before the introduction of the Ground Protection Act, legislation concerned with groundwater quality was fragmentary and incomplete. Detailed provisions regarding drinking water quality are laid down in the Waterworks Decree, introduced in 1984 to supersede a 1960 regulation, in order to implement the EC directive. This directive, in effect, lowered the maximum admissible concentration of nitrate in drinking water in the Netherlands from 100 mg/l to 50 mg/l.

The first break-through of the environmentally-oriented opposition occurred in 1984 when the Minister of Agriculture unexpectedly introduced a ban on the establishment and extension of pig and poultry units. The farmers interpreted this more as a break of trust by 'their' department.

Adoption of the Ground Protection Act is a typical example of Dutch consensus politics. The search for compromise which characterizes Dutch policy making also makes it a lengthy process. This is shown by the time-lag of roughly 15 years between the first presentation of a draft version to parliament and the final introduction of the Act in 1987. With the introduction of the Ground Protection Act the wishes of the farmers are taken into consideration once again. The legislative norms introduced in the legislation are quite flexible, so as to give farmers time to adjust to the new constraints.

This concern for the farmer's position extends so wide that in the special water protection areas the water supply companies (i.e. the consumers) are asked to meet the bill if farmers have to switch over to environmentally more acceptable fertilizer levels. The willingness of the water companies to do so is, understandably, not great. The water companies are already making much effort to adhere to the limits imposed on nitrate content by taking a number of expensive technical measures (van der Kley and Bennett, 1988).

With the Fertilizers Act, which became effective on 1 May 1987, a system of charges has been introduced whereby farmers must pay an amount based on the quality of wastes produced above a given quantity, according on its phosphate content. To enable effective enforcement of these limits, each farmer is required to maintain a record of the quantity of wastes produced and to provide information about the available land, the extent of the wastes surplus and its transportation and sale to others.

In the Animal Wastes Action Programme the Ministers of Agriculture and Environment in 1987 outlined proposals for spending an extra Nfl. 40 million annually for a period of four years in order to reduce the animal wastes surplus. The bulk of the money (Nfl. 15 million/year) will be spent on the creation of manure storage capacity with the development of both individual and centrally planned storage facilities. These are needed mainly during the winter months when, as a result of the Ground Protection Act, farmers are forbidden to apply animal wastes to the land.

In addition, research and operational projects will be supported dealing with

o reducing manure and mineral surpluses by lowering mineral concentrations in cattle fodder;
o central treatment, aimed at either converting or destroying animal wastes;
o promoting the sale and market for treated animal waste products.

The possibility of incinerating animal wastes or dumping them at sea, discussed in the early 1980s, is meanwhile out of the question for the time being as it is seen to represent simply a shift of an environmental problem from one medium to another.

These governmental measures to limit overfertilization will take many years to actually lower nitrate concentrations in extracted groundwater. So, corrective measures on the waterside will be needed in the near future to reduce the nitrate load of drinking water. These include closing water extraction points, blending drinking water, and the application of existing costly nitrate removal techniques.

In sum, the Dutch government has been forced to take the nitrate problem very seriously. Whereas 'nitrate policy' used to be fragmentary and incomplete, it has now become more coherent and appropriate.

The aim of the governmental measures imposed on livestock farmers is to reduce the nitrate load in groundwater and to reach, in the year 2000, the ideal situation whereby nitrogen is applied at a level that meets crop demand. By then, technical solutions should be available to dispose of or diminish the enormous animal waste surplus created by these measures.

An interesting measure which has not been discussed yet is the introduction of a tax on mineral fertilizers. However, irrespective of the measures being introduced at the moment, it is inevitable that nitrates will continue to leach out and further contaminate the deeper groundwater and, thus, endanger drinking water supplies. The drinking water companies are responding to this situation by taking measures to remove the contamination already present in their water resources. As such, they can only cure the symptoms. Techniques for the removal of nitrate are in an advanced phase. If they have to be applied, the consumer will notice it in increased bills. The alternative appears little better for the consumer. The water supply companies and, consequently, the consumer will have to pay for any loss of income when farmers are required to switch to environmentally acceptable fertilization levels in water protection areas.

In the Netherlands, the government has tackled the nitrate problem by means of legislation. A first step was the introduction of a two-year ban on the establishment and extension of intensive pig and poultry units in 1984. Unfortunately, this did not lead to a decline in animal waste production. On the contrary, the animal waste production by pigs increased considerably. In 1987, this temporary 'Pig and Poultry Holdings Limitation Act' was replaced by and became subsumed in the Fertilizers Act. Together with the Ground Protection Act it constitutes the main framework intended to restrain the production and utilization of animal wastes. In this latest Act, a distinction is made between general and special protection levels in water catchment areas for which the provincial governments are required to draw up plans. Much debate preceded the realization of these Acts. On the one hand, there are the water supply companies and environmentalists who are very anxious to reduce nitrogen inputs into the soil. On the other hand, there are the farmers who do not want to yield to mandatory governmental measures aimed at restricting the application of animal wastes to the soil without government compensation for loss of income.

The outcome of the initial debate was typical of Dutch policy making. A kind of compromise was reached, whereby all interest groups had to make concessions. Limits were imposed on the application of animal wastes, but they were not as strict as originally intended, especially not from an environmental point of view. The new measures were quite generous to farmers in that they gave them time to adjust to the new constraints. Provisions for compensating farmers for loss of income are made only with respect to special protection areas. The precise form of such financial compensation is still the subject of controversy and debate. The water supply companies are not automatically going to pay the bill (van der Kley and Bennett, 1988).

Notes

1. The old British policy was to allow a three month moving average below 80 mg/l.
2. For details see Bruckmeier, 1987a, 1987b, 1987c, 1987d, 1988a; Brüggemann et al., 1986; Conrad, 1988a, Gitschel, 1987a, 1987b, 1987c; Hafenecker, 1989; Hünermann, 1987; Teherani-Krönner, 1988a, 1988b, 1988c, 1988d; Uka 1989.
3. These adjectives characterize the dominant regulatory style referring to the inclusion or exclusion of the public and environmental groups, to the existence of implementation coalitions or the dominance of one political actor, and to the delegation of problem solving by 'delocalizing' it, by waiting for solutions 'from above', or by denying the problem.

5 Nitrate pollution and politics in comparison

After having discussed the national situations of Great Britain, the Federal Republic of Germany and the Netherlands, the last two sections of this report attempt to compare these situations. Chapter 6 remains largely at a descriptive level, whereas more systematic and analytical comparative conclusions are drawn in the last chapter.

The structure of the nitrate problem

The structure of the nitrate problem varies in each country according to the regional pattern of agricultural production, soils, hydrogeology and water supply. In Great Britain, the nitrate problem is apparent mainly in the south-east, where high doses of mineral fertilizer are applied, substrata are very permeable, and groundwater is the main source of drinking water. In the Netherlands, the problem is located essentially in the eastern and southern parts of the country where very intensive livestock farming coincides with huge amounts of animal manure and permeable sandy soils. Groundwater dominates as the source of drinking water everywhere in the Netherlands. In the Federal Republic of Germany, the situation is somewhat more complex. Nitrate contamination of groundwater, the main source of drinking water especially in the northern parts of the FRG, occurs in particular in local areas of intense livestock farming on permeable soils, and especially in private wells. Huge amounts of liquid animal manure from intense livestock farming are often spread over agricultural land but fortunately these soils are less permeable than in the Netherlands. In the middle and southern parts of West Germany, it is frequently the coincidence of intensive special cropping such as vegetables and viticulture, but sometimes also 'normal' mixed farming with permeable soils and local groundwater use, where nitrate contamination of drinking water is observed. Therefore, the German situation of nitrate pollution is a more scattered one than in the two other countries.

In these parts of the three countries and elsewhere, nitrate levels have more or less continuously risen during the last few decades, and several drinking water wells have had to be closed down. Depending on the respective hydrogeological conditions, preventive measures would solve the nitrate problem relatively quickly or only after decades. Here, Great Britain appears relatively to be in the best position. To a lower degree, the same seems to hold true, in general, for the severity of the nitrate problem. It is probably most serious for the Netherlands, and there substantial remedial measures will probably be most costly. In the Federal Republic of Germany, the situation varies considerably from area to area.

In all three countries, nitrate in ground and drinking water is seen as the major problem of nitrate pollution. In the Netherlands, ammonia emissions from animal manure and nitrate levels in vegetables also receive serious attention and official concern. The contamination of surface water by animal wastes also creates concern over drinking water quality in some parts of the UK. Environmental problems of nitrate pollution, however, may still turn out to be considerable in the longer run, as in 1988 the publicly realized problem of north sea pollution by nitrates may indicate, but, for the moment, are best dealt with at a scientific research level in most cases. The health hazards of high nitrate levels are still considered at worst 'unproven' and of minor importance in Britain, whereas they are taken somewhat more seriously in the two other countries despite the lack of unequivocal medical evidence.

The nitrate debate

It is reasonable to speak of a nitrate debate in all three countries sharing a similar general pattern, but differing significantly in detail. The nitrate problem is overwhelmingly seen as a medical hazard due to higher nitrate concentrations in drinking water which stem from agriculturally-induced nitrate washout into groundwater. Only in the Netherlands, are other related aspects, such as nitrate in vegetables and ammonia emissions from agriculture, discussed outside of expert circles. Whereas the nitrate problem received broader scientific recognition in the 1970s, it became an issue of public debate only during the 1980s, though of varying local, regional and national intensity. The rise of the nitrate debate was connected with a number of events.

These included the introduction of the EC drinking water directive in 1980, which lowered the nitrate standard to 50 mg/l, increasing nitrate concentrations in groundwater, the closure of some public wells with nitrate levels and a growing public and political concern about the environmental problems of agriculture. Nitrate contamination of groundwater is perceived as a typical and eminent example of the problems associated with modern agriculture in the FRG and the Netherlands, but less so in the UK.

This difference has to do with the perceived lower severity of the nitrate problem and a belief that there are no health hazards associated with nitrate concentrations between 50 and 100 mg/l in the UK. Only in the Netherlands, did environmental groups play an important role in initiating and broadening the nitrate debate, whereas their significance input to the debate was less and occurred later in Great Britain and the FRG. Local nitrate controversies played some role in the Federal Republic of Germany, whereas nitrate is a more regional issue in Great Britain and in the Netherlands. Of course there has been a national debate in each country. Controversy, in particular, has focussed on the existence of a health risk, the kind of remedial measures to be preferred, the distribution of their costs, and the necessity for significant changes in agricultural production to solve the nitrate problem. Primarily, the conflict is one between agriculturalists (farmers, fertilizer industry, agricultural organizations and authorities, food industry) and water related groups (water suppliers, water authorities, water protection groups, health authorities).

Differences between the countries have to do also with the different structure of the nitrate problem. It is one of mineral fertilizer in Great Britain, one of animal manure in the Netherlands and both in different regions of the FRG. There are differences in the regulations debated and pursued, in the institutional structures, the distribution of the competence and legal jurisdiction in different national political cultures and policy styles (e.g. more legalistic approaches in the FRG and the Netherlands and more informal agreements in the UK). The intensity of the nitrate debate appears to correlate with the perceived seriousness of the nitrate problem - highest in the Netherlands, lowest in Great Britain. From a broader, superficial viewpoint, the similarities in the national nitrate debates seem to be more striking than the national differences, although this perspective may certainly change with a more detailed comparison.

Nitrate politics

Since politics normally is more closely related to specific policy measures and regulations, it is no surprise that national differences are greater than among the nitrate debates. Similarities show up again at the general level of politics. Thus, there was little political action in the

1970s, but considerable political conflict in the 1980s. Only the British delegation voiced scepticism at the proposed lower nitrate standard within the bargaining process over the new EC drinking water directive during the 1970s. The main political conflict occurred between the proponents of agricultural interests and those of water supply and protection. In most cases, politics refer more to formal policy actions and regulations than to substantive measures and implementation which is, yet, of little actual relevance.

In Great Britain, the political process around nitrate largely occurs via a private (informal) interaction and bargaining process between administrative and associated actors. This is less so in the Federal Republic of Germany and the Netherlands although informal bargaining and decision-making processes are also of central importance in these countries. Another feature of politics has to do with differences in institutional structures and political cultures. In Great Britian, political decision-making is very centralized at the national level. In the FRG, the states (*Länder*) play an essential role in nitrate politics mainly because of their jurisdiction over water management. In the Netherlands, the situation is similar, but somewhat more nationally centralized. In addition, informal interaction plays a greater role in this small country where every relevant actor knows every other relevant one. In nitrate politics, hardly any joint action or strategy has developed between water utilities and environmentalists. Especially in the FRG, local nitrate controversy was frequently initiated by environmental action groups based on accusations of nitrate standard violations by water utilities and of too little action on the part of the responsible health authorities. Farmers and farming practices remained largely outside the controversy.

The political process - more formal in the FRG and the Netherlands and more informal in Great Britain - tends to develop in a direction where the nitrate problem is taken more serious and the resulting pressure demands more efficient and less detrimental fertilization techniques. This is coupled with demands for the installation of water protection zones where farmers are compensated for restrictions on farming, and for corrective water treatment measures as well as temporary derogations from the nitrate standards.

In the UK, nitrate politics is moulded by two central issues, privatization of the water authorities and, to a somewhat lower degree, the attempts to reconciliate agricultural supply and demand in agricultural policy. In the FRG, issues of central importance are the cost distribution of preventive measures, especially in water protection zones (e.g. the water penny debate), limitations on spreading liquid animal manure by liquid manure ordinances, and the income situation of farmers. In the Netherlands, nitrate politics has developed into a field in its own right to a larger extent than in the other two countries. Here, it is strongly connected with the storage, treatment and distribution of animal manure, with the profitability of Dutch agriculture and its exports, and with groundwater protection in general. These crucial issues have certainly influenced the development of nitrate politics and policy and partly explain the observable national differences.

Despite the polarization of nitrate politics between agriculturalists and 'water people', the attempts to achieve a pragmatic consensus are considerable, though only partly successful. The most advanced example is the Netherlands, as described in chapter 4. This obviously has to do with the dominant Dutch policy style.

As a result, nitrate debates and politics contributed to rising environmental concerns in agriculture and to a more serious recognition of the nitrate problem. Substantive changes in actual nitrate pollution can be observed only to a minor degree up to the present, though possibly this should improve in the future. Nitrate politics can also be interpreted as a scape-goat policy game about the costs of solving the nitrate problem. As long as all actors succeed in passing the buck, the solution of the problem will certainly be delayed.

Nitrate policy

It is unreasonable up to the present to speak of a real nitrate policy in the countries investigated. At best, the Netherlands provides an example of an evolving nitrate policy in its own right. Therefore, nitrate policy is used as an analytical term only in this book and refers to those policy efforts which relate to the nitrate problem. These differ considerably in the three countries, although some similarities can be seen at a more general level.

British nitrate policy was and is concerned with: finally adopting and implementing the EC drinking water directive; fixing and defending derogations from the nitrate standard; developing a code of good agricultural practice; organizing responsibility for and control of water quality in the light of the intended privatization of the British water authorities; recommending water protection zones without burdening farmers; pushing corrective measures to deal with the nitrate problem onto the water side. British nitrate policy involves a lot of tactical political manoeuvering but little actual policy implementation yet. In effect, the nitrate problem is not yet perceived to be a very serious and as little pressure as is politically viable is exerted on the farmers, though the situation is going to change since late 1987.

German nitrate policy is rather legalistically orientated. The revision of the drinking water ordinance, the amendment to the water management act, the water penny, the liquid manure ordinances, the official attempts to define good agricutural practice as well as farming restrictions in water protection zones have to be mentioned here. In addition, attempts to achieve more efficient and environmentally compatible fertilization practices, including the N_{min}-method, through the agricultural advisory service are relevant, too.

There is somewhat more pressure on agriculture to contribute to the solution of the nitrate problem than in Great Britain, though with strong local variations. Some implementation of the above policy efforts, more on the water side than by agriculture, can be observed.

Dutch nitrate policy is also dominated by legal approaches to the nitrate problem along with the installation and subsidizing of animal waste treatment facilities and provisions for keeping records of manure production. The major legal efforts were the two-year ban on the extension of pig and poultry units, the Ground Protection Act and the Fertilizers Act. These primarily affected farmers but left a lot of leeway in order to avoid severe restrictions on agriculture. Dutch nitrate policy, therefore, can not overcome the need for water-related measures in order to comply with the nitrate standard in the short run, but at least plans to dump animal manure in the sea have been abandoned. Differences between the Netherlands and the other countries can be seen in the fact that, at least formally, the dominant policy effort to solve the nitrate problem involves preventive agricultural measures. One may doubt their substantial success to date.

Comparing these national policies, one meets various legal, institutional, cultural, nitrate problem related differences but similar objectives too, as pointed out in the previous section. Great Britain, the Federal Republic of Germany and the Netherlands, form a general trend of increasing viability and orientation towards changes in agricultural practices in nitrate policy. However, actual implementation of these policy efforts have only partly occurred in the past, especially when agriculture is the regulation's addressee.

Local problem regulation

In the last resort, nitrate pollution of groundwater is *prima facie* a local problem. Dealing with this problem through local water utilities, the local water, health or agricultural administration, local farmers and the local population and this can be achieved by using existing regulatory instruments or by developing new ones, will differ from case to case. In general, the more centralized the regulation of the nitrate problem nationally, the fewer differences in the pattern of local problem regulation can be expected.

Nevertheless, even in Great Britain local activities led to more problem awareness and administrative action in the London case by the Anglian Water Authority and, to a lower degree, by the Yorkshire Water Authority (Aaranovitch, 1988; Baldock, 1988; Wathern, 1988b). In those regions which are concerned with the nitrate problem, the activities undertaken in the past, remained largely only those of the water authorities. The strategies of the different water authorities differed considerably, and only recently the picture is starting to change in the direction of more similar and more strenuous approaches towards the problem by the water authorities and the (environmental) administration.

For the FRG with less centralization, the particular local constellations which have formed do not allow unequivocal conclusions concerning regulatory styles to be made (Bruckmeier, 1987a, 1988a). Also the different states approach the problem of nitrate regulation quite differently, as indicated in chapter 4.

In the Netherlands, different concrete approaches at the level of the provinces, also exist, e.g. for the implementation of the Ground Protection Act (van der Kley and Bennett, 1988). At a local level, the existing structures of agriculture and water supply as well as the engagement of the local population certainly play a role. However, without local case studies no unequivocal statements can be made.

In general, local efforts to keep to the nitrate standard by water related measures predominate. These may be supplemented by more or less stringent attempts to influence agricultural practices, in some cases with legally available instruments, e.g. the ability to prohibit spreading animal manure in winter. Occasionally, local administration proceeds further than intended by the government though with a high risk of being whistled back by the higher authority (cf. Teherani-Krönner, 1988b). In sum, variations in local problem regulation are due, at least as much, to local specifities as to national differences between the countries investigated.

Environmental counselling

In all three countries, environmental counselling in the agrarian sector developed through processes of reorientation and differentiation of the traditional agricultural advisory systems. The process of development can be seen as one of gradual increase of concern for environmental problems within the traditional task structure of the advisory services, where up to now focus is laid on economic and farm-management-problems.

The core structure of agricultural counselling are the official, governmental or 'semi-governmental' advisory services which have the most widespread networks of services.[1]

Up to now, no official or legal redefinition of the goals of the advisory services happened and the inclusion of environmental counselling happens in more informal ways, e.g. changing information and recommendations about the amount of fertilizers or about techniques of fertilization in order to prevent intake losses and washout. Therefore, it is difficult to evaluate the role of environmental counselling within the range of nitrate policy.[2] In general, for all countries, it may be said, that the advisory system has rather stable organizational structures and is able to fullfil - or to compete with - different goals of agricultural policy.

The beginning of reorientation of the advisory systems was in the 1970s, but only in the 1980s it can be said that environmental problems became more significant within the tasks of the consultants (Bruckmeier, 1988b).

The institutional structures of the advisory system are complicated and differ from country to country, due to reasons of historical developments and different political, administrative and legal traditions.

In the UK, the core of the agricultural advisory services is ADAS (Agriculture Development Advisory Services), which, after a reorganization in 1987 (privatization), is no longer a public institution and since then changes the farmers demanding advice with fees. ADAS offers all kinds of advice (through mass media, printed information, group and individual advice) but only individual advice has significance and is demanded by farmers as it can fulfill the level of specificity and supply detailed information farmers want, but which other forms of advice don't have. The goal orientation of ADAS lies within the scope of traditional goals mentioned above, which, after the inclusion of environmental advice, follows the rule 'economy first, than ecology'. ADAS propagates an information policy 'in the best economic interest of the individual farmer'. The practical problems and action deficits of ADAS are of the kind that not all farmers get advice, the selectivity being is one in favour of competent farmers, well-managed and big farms.

In the FRG, there is a more complicated organizational structure of the advisory services than in the UK, as they are different from one federal state to another. Broadly seen, there are two forms of advisory services which go under the heading 'official agricultural advisory services': in the states of south Germany, there are governmental services, in north Germany, they are part of the self-government of agriculturalists and run by the Chambers of Agriculture. It is also in nothern Germany, that the special form of 'Ringberatung' exists which is a specialized form of counselling that a limited number of farmers organizes by themselves, who also pay for their own consultant. It is only within this structure that a specialized advisory service for ecological farm management - and only one up to now - exists. In contrast to ADAS, the German services up to now operate without fees.

In the Netherlands, environmental counselling is also a minor part within the well established Dutch system of advisory services. But it is already more developed than in the UK and West Germany, especially since corresponding efforts have been made during recent years. The advice is essentially free of charge for the farmer. Environmental counselling refers to nitrate washout, ammonia emissions, and the new Dutch laws on fertilizer and on ground protection, in particular. It is provided in two main ways: documentary information is drawn up and distributed by the Centre for Agriculture and Environment at Utrecht which receives a grant for this work from the ministry. The agricultural ministry's own advisory services regularly visit farmers and provide practical advice of minimizing environmental impacts.[3]

In comparison and in general, it may be said that environmental counselling with regard to the nitrate problem is not very intensive and not very efficient in all countries. Even in the FRG, where more investigation and analysis of the advisory services seem to exist, no exact empirical data are available on how effective the system is. But there are many doubts that environmental counselling can be done effectively. It is not only the still lacking importance that it has within the scope of economically-based counselling goals, also the lack of man-power, decreasing capacities of the services and the problem that the services do not reach all farmers, just the ones demanding for it, which provide together for limited success (Bruckmeier, 1988b).

Notes

1. Environmental advice with regard to agriculture is offered by a variety of organizations and institutions. Besides the state-run services, at least some private agents must be mentioned, among which the advisory services of firms, especially of the fertilizer industry, are the most important ones. For more detailed description of the whole range of organizations see Bruckmeier, 1987e (for the FRG), Gitay and Wathern, 1988 (for the UK).
2. This can be done to some degree by analysis of the various functions of the advisory system and by using the rare empirical data on the performance and effectiveness of counselling; see Bruckmeier, 1987e (for the FRG).
3. The Dutch advisory system has not been analyzed within the research project 'Increasing Environmental Concern in Agricultural Policy'.

6 Comparative conclusions

The significance of the nitrate problem in the agriculture-environment debate

The significance of the nitrate problem for the agriculture-environment debate should be evaluated on three levels. First, how serious is nitrate pollution of groundwater compared with other environmental problems caused by agriculture? Second, how seriously is the nitrate problem considered in the agriculture-environment debate? Third, what is the possible impact of the nitrate debate on the evolution of the agriculture-environment debate and of agricultural environmental policy and practices?

As stated in chapter 5, the severity of the nitrate problem obviously increases in the sequence Great Britain, the Federal Republic of Germany, the Netherlands. Nitrate pollution is a problem locally or regionally and is strongly connected with agricultural intensity. The chances for its solution without enormous changes in agricultural practice decrease in the sequence FRG, Great Britain, the Netherlands. This is due to differences in the local occurrance of specific combinations of agricultural production, hydrogeological conditions and groundwater use.

The significance of the nitrate problem in the individual national agriculture-environment debates varies from being of secondary importance in Great Britain to being one of the most prominent issues in the FRG and the Netherlands. In each country, however, the public concern and the intensity of the discussion about nitrates has considerably increased in the

1980s. At the same time, the nitrate problem has largely remained a concern over the health risk of nitrate-polluted ground and drinking water. Other potential detrimental aspects have hardly been discussed yet. One may also question whether the prominence of the nitrate debate, induced among other things by rising nitrate levels and the reduction in the nitrate standard, does not somewhat deflect concern over other more important environmental implications of agriculture in the agriculture-environment debate, especially those of cumulative and synergetic effects of agricultural production. Looking at the social structure and dynamics of public debates, this latter problem may be relativized if the nitrate debates acts in a pathfinder role for the increasing significance of environmental concerns in agriculture.

In the long run, such indirect (symbolic) impacts of the nitrate debate and nitrate politics may be more important than their direct effects in solving the nitrate problem. So, the self-dynamics of the nitrate debate may contribute to the gradual change of agricultural practices towards greater environmental compatibility during the years to come. It is then, however, but one piece in a general social process. From this perspective, wildlife and habitat issues may play a functionally-equivalent pathfinder role in Great Britain. What counts in this context is the overall medium-term impact upon rising environmental concern and management in agriculture. Since it is hardly possible to prove such hypotheses empirically, one can only guess at this probable impact of the nitrate problem and debate upon the development of an environmentally more compatible agriculture. Only in retrospective will more definite conclusions be possible.

The actors

Considering the interests of the relevant actors, it becomes clear, at least partly, why preventive regulation of the nitrate problem has been only of secondary importance until now. An oversimplified view is that the rather straightforward and well-organized interests of the agricultural community meet only relatively diffuse and ambiguous interests on the part of the opposing side, primarily water utilities, public health authorities, and environmentalists.

Agriculturists tend to prefer regional and local, that is, differentiated and not general, problem solutions. This facilitates defending the *status quo* and accepting restrictions only with financial compensation and administrative support. Furthermore, compensation payments may offer a new source of agricultural subsidies in times when traditional sources tend not to be increasing.

The interests of the water utilities as the main opponents of agriculture are more ambiguous. They certainly prefer low nitrate concentrations, but also weak standards. In the beginning, they had no interest in raising the prominence of a public debate which posed a threat to the image of clean and healthy water everywhere. This was not primarily an economic position. As water prices are more or less publicly regulated, water utilities can, more or less, pass on price increases to the consumer. However, privatization of the water industry in the UK may fundamentally change this position.

For environmentalists, the nitrate problem is but one issue of environmental pollution to be attacked. Only in the Netherlands, was the nitrate issue taken up in the early 1970s by environmental organizations. Here they played a significant role in nitrate politics. In the UK, the Friends of the Earth came late to the debate, not until the 1980s, and with little effect, while German environmental groups have yet to play a significant role.

Water and public health authorities can usually regulate and control drinking water distribution, but not agriculture. They, therefore, tend to seek corrective solutions to the nitrate problem. They also often have no interest in making a big case out of the nitrate issue, because this could lead to their being criticized for failing to carry out their task properly. Similarly, local communes affected by high NO_3 concentrations in drinking water will often tend to play down long-term problems in order to protect their image as healthy and attractive tourist resorts.

For many other actors involved in the nitrate policy game, such as the fertilizer industry, food industry, agricultural trade companies, agricultural machinery industry, agricultural administration, consumer associations, parties, courts, agricultural, environmental, water, and medical research institutions, the nitrate issue is only of relatively minor relevance. Only recently have these actors started to take a position on which type of solution to this problem they favour. However, actors from the agricultural sector developed their position much earlier in order to prevent injury to their interests.

A few actors have vested interests *vis-à-vis* the nitrate problem, primarily agriculture and to a lesser degree water utilities, the fertilizer industry and agricultural administration. One should also mention the EC bureaucracy which is keen to see its directives implemented at the national level, at least formally. In the British case, however, the General Directorate for Environment played an important role in nitrate politics and policy by forcing abandonment of certain proposed implementation procedures over MAC and derogations. To a lesser degree, this holds true for West Germany more recently, too, as indicated in chapter 4. In view of this constellation of interests, indicated schematically for the FRG in Figure 6.1, it is no wonder that there is only a limited overall interest in a preventive problem solution on the side of agriculture. This situation is further enhanced by the fact that actors within a particular policy arena (e.g. agricultural or water policy) usually have no interest in having their scope for policy decisions narrowed by additional boundary conditions or even by new actors.

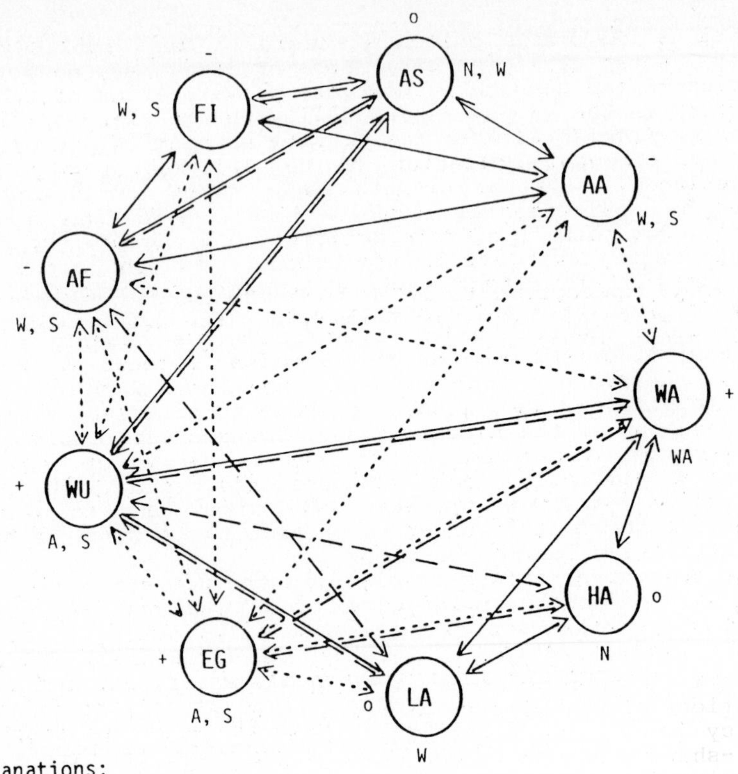

Explanations:

AA	Agricultural Authorities
AF	Agriculture, Farmers
AS	Public Agricultural Advisory Services
EG	Environmental Groups
FI	Fertilizer Industry
HA	Health Authorities
LA	Local Administration
WA	Water Authorities
WU	Water Utilities (affected)

+ actor	in favor of strong (and preventive) action, including himself to solve the nitrate problem
- actor	not in favor of active (and preventive) action,
o actor	little involvement, open attitude
f,w,s,n	costs should be paid by farmers (f), water utilities (w), state (s); no clear opinion (n)
———	actor strategies mostly in relative harmony
-------	primarily antagonistic actor strategies
— — —	unclear, ambivalent, but existing relations

Figure 6.1 Schematic actor configuration in nitrate politics in the mid-1980s

Nevertheless, the pattern of behaviour of the actors has tended to allow more interaction and exchange of information in recent years. Whereas some agreement on the facts of the nitrate issue can now be observed, the controversy increasingly focuses on the *nervus rerum* of the interests of the main actors in nitrate policy, namely who is going to pay the costs of the problem solution, whichever one is chosen?

As a result, the manifest interests in a preventive solution to the nitrate problem on the side of agriculture can be expected to be sufficiently to force adoption only if the problem is perceived to be a very serious one. In the case of the Federal Republic of Germany and the Netherlands, this is in areas of intensive animal husbandry.

Policy games around nitrate

Policy games around nitrate, by and large, developed within the established channels of the political and administrative system. Typical features of these policy games include: consideration for the interests of farmers; generous implementation and control of mandatory standards; priority for water related solutions; clear distribution of roles, participation and competences among the actors; preference for generalized legal regulations in West Germany and the Netherlands apart from moral suasion; only loose coupling of the formal interests of most actors to specific substantive solutions of the nitrate problem. Due to the dynamics of the policy game, the strategies chosen by the actors to avoid cost-sharing change accordingly. Trends at the meta-level of changing the rules of the policy games in the Federal Republic of Germany have been indicated in chapter 4. The situation in the Netherlands and - to a lesser degree - in Great Britain is relatively similar.

Overall, it is more the institutionalized political structure, withinputs in the terminology of Easton (1965), than the difference in power of the relevant actors which leads to the observed asymmetry in the pattern of interest consideration in nitrate policy. The structural disadvantage of environmental interests in environmental policy, as well as of the institutionalized consideration of environmental concerns in other policy areas which can be observed in general, also takes effect in nitrate policy. The actual power and influence of agriculturalists and water utilities, however, do not seem to differ considerably. Although symbolic nitrate policy has often dominated over substantive nitrate policy, when seen against the proclaimed goal of a preventive problem solution on the side of agriculture, the efforts towards substantive policy measures have clearly increased. This has to do with a slowly growing consensus between the relevant nitrate policy actors which can be explained by their strategic reasoning (see Conrad, 1988b). After an early phase involving the non-observance and a playing-down of the nitrate problem by most actors, there was a period when agriculturalists strictly refused any restrictions on their activities. At this time, the water utilities insisted on the application of the polluter-pays principle and the government limited its activities to symbolic policy and funding of research and development. This, in turn, led to an aggravation of the nitrate problem. Only during recent years policy strategies are being applied, where all actors have made concessions, thereby, improving the chances for compromize solutions.

The specific conditions and features of the policy games around nitrate clearly differ for the three countries investigated. Apart from the lower concern about nitrate pollution in the UK until 1987, the above characteristics nevertheless apply more or less to each country. Significant differences have already been mentioned in a previous chapter. The main features are the more informal and less legal orientation of British nitrate politics; the strong consensus orientation of Dutch political culture, which made the 'interim wet' during 1984 a complete surprise and disappointment for Dutch agriculture; the relevance of federal states in nitrate policy in the Federal Republic of Germany.

In sum, the major differences in the national policy games around nitrate can be seen in the prominent role of environmentalists in the Netherlands, the informal and hesistant policy process in Great Britain (coming close to a non-decision policy) and the affiliation of nitrate politics with varying superior national concerns. Political parties and their differences played only a minor role in the nitrate policy game.

The permanent and increasing crisis over the Common Agricultural Policy will probably affect the public debate on the environmental problems of modern agriculture and increase the chances of some ecological adaptation. Thus, increasing environmental concern in agricultural policy may have a better chance as a by-product of budgetary or economically-influenced measures in agriculture rather than as a straightforward environmental policy program lacking a powerful constituency where the risk of mere symbolic policy is considerable.

Policy instruments and implementation

In the field of nitrate policy, the policy instruments used are the typical ones utilized by governmental environmental policy. These include: funding appropriate research and demonstration projects; extension of advice on fertilizer use to take account of groundwater protection; setting nitrate standards, including (temporary) derogations; public control of standard violations; legal provisions for compensation payments for farming restrictions; enhancement of procedures to install water protection zones; restrictions on agriculture in these protection zones; development of codes of good agricultural practice; management agreements in favour of environmentally compatible agricultural practices; liquid manure ordinances; administrative help and funds for the establishment of animal manure storage, transportation and processing facilities; charges or taxes on fertilizer use; judicial sanctions for persons or organizations which do not follow the regulations.

The relative weight and the specific design of these policy instruments vary not only between the countries, but also between different regions within a country. In England, the use of these policy instruments is less advanced and more informal, yet but does not show significant differences to the other countries at this general level of comparison. For instance, the water authorities are responsible for water supply and water quality control in the UK under the Water Act. This situation will change with privatization with the separation of the supply and regulatory functions in accordance with the situation in the other two countries. However, the principles of the control process are not so different in practice when compared with the other countries. As already stated, the process of policy implementation in most cases is not yet very advanced and knowledge about actual implementation is usually insufficient. So, it is difficult to judge the adequacy of the policy instruments which are intended for use. For instance, the emphasis on moral suasion in nitrate policy may not be a very effective policy instrument when addressing farmers because compliance is purely voluntarily while the emphasis on financial incentives is not in accordance with the polluter-pays principle. However, in view of the considerable veto power of the agricultural community *vis-à-vis* environmental policy and of the political and social culture as well as the economic situation prevalent in the farming community, the combination of these two policy instruments may well turn out to be an appropriate strategy.

Policy implementation is most advanced in the regulation of the drinking water standard. Animal manure ordinances have been partially successful in prohibiting the spreading of manure in winter time. Regulations in water protection zones are starting to be adopted while environmental counselling and charges on fertilizer use have been discussed. Altogether, however, the development of unequivocal policy instruments and policy implementation is less advanced in the UK than in the FRG and the Netherlands. As long as political decision-makers are only intent on setting signals for an agriculture which is environmentally more compatible and not on controlling its development, they need not be concerned about inadequate policy implementation. From the viewpoint of the environmentalist, however, these deficiencies in policy instruments and implementation certainly are much more serious and can be interpreted as policy failure. For farmers the loopholes in nitrate policy instruments and regulation may just be the remedy necessary to live with these provisions if they can no longer be prevented. This does not hold true for the environmentally-oriented farmers who are but a minority at present.

The pattern and deficiencies of regulation

Overall, the pattern of nitrate regulation corresponds to the dominant pattern of environmental policy regulation. The regulation of the nitrate problem occurs mainly in a reactive and corrective manner, with the water utilities concerned as the main actors. The provision of a legal framework and fixed standards plays an important role in accordance with the legalistic German and Dutch conditions of mandatory regulation including nitrate standard in drinking water regulations and water protection area and liquid manure ordinances. This is much less so in Great Britain, but because of the legally-binding provisions of the EC directive, there is also a tendency in this direction. It is more the violation of a legal standard than the need to resolve actual problems specific to local circumstances which mostly forces responsible authorities to act.

Somewhat less typical in the pattern of nitrate regulations are the following points:

1. The openness and responsiveness of the political system *vis-à-vis* local problem articulation and different interests was, despite the avoidance and filtering of such concerns, comparatively large. This had to do with the growing sensitivity of environmental policy with respect to groundwater protection (cf. LAWA, 1987).
2. The funding of and even promoting nitrate research is certainly above average in the FRG and the Netherlands. As a result the available knowledge for nitrate regulation is now rather broad and extensive.
3. Relatively large opportunities for local and informal regulations of the nitrate problem still exist. At present these fail not because of rigid generalized formal prescriptions and rules but because of local interest coalitions and conflicts.

In sum, the pattern of nitrate regulation can be characterized as gradually evolving, more or less segmented, regulations of drinking water. These regulations slowly expand by the application of legal norms and standards from health and water policy to agriculture. Consideration of the impacts of agricultural policy and economics is excluded with the important exception of compensation payments to farmers. At the politic level the formal implementation of such regulations appears to be more relevant than their actual effectiveness.

The overall pattern of nitrate regulation may be evaluated as follows:

1. Since the health and environmental significance of the nitrate problem at present can be judged as only a secondary one, compared to other pollutants, the lack of a very rigorous regulation cannot be viewed negatively.
2. Preventive regulations are pursued less stringently than corrective ones on the water side. This need not imply a negative evaluation because of the lack of political

viability of any cause-oriented regulation and the time lag before it would have any effect. Deficiencies in this approach cannot be denied in view of the often higher costs of water related measures, their limited scope and the fact that much of the knowledge about the main issues was already available to the bureaucracy in the 1970s.

3. Substantive regulations were developed late and in a re-active manner compared with the duration of the nitrate debate. However, this time delay is not unusual when one considers the minor significance of the nitrate problem, the lack of an established agricultural environmental policy in the 1970s, and the existence of a nitrate standard of approximately 100 mg/l already in the 1970s.
4. Whereas water related measures are usually effective, but limited to the nitrate content in drinking water, the ecological effectiveness of other measures is generally limited both in space and size.
5. The dominance of water-related measures and the uncertain success of information campaigns and advisory efforts make the existing nitrate regulation relatively inefficient, compared to other available measures, such as rigorous restrictions in extended water protection zones.
6. Whereas the control of the drinking water quality is feasible for the administration, alternatives such as the implementation of the liquid manure ordinances and the regulation of water protection zones involve many difficulties for the responsible authorities.
7. The process of policy formulation and implementation was typical of rather closed program formation and decision-making involving small circles of bureaucrats, agricultural and water lobbyists and experts. As such, the process was not really open to public participation, except to a certain degree in the Netherlands.
8. Splitting the competences and the segmentation of activities did not facilitate solving the nitrate problem. However, in view of the lack of any nitrate-specific organization with the administration at large and the availability of the necessary knowledge and competence within the enforcement authorities, this situation need not be negatively evaluated.
9. The available resources for nitrate policy are large in view of the general scarcity of public resources. However, their distribution with the preference for regulations requiring many resources, led to few being available for the actual implementation.
10. The coordination of nitrate policy measures and their embedding in broader agricultural environmental policy programs is rather bad.
11. The distribution of competences is without major problems with regard to the different levels of policy. This is not so in the functional dimension where environmental agencies and water authorities sometimes lack clear-cut responsibilities.

12. Despite many difficulties of enforcement and control, all regulations were politically viable against the strong resistance of the affected parties. Political viability is partly achieved by watering down the regulations, by compensation payments, and by reliance on moral suasion.
13. The substantive contribution of most regulations to the solution of the nitrate problem is often limited. Water-related measures are at least more unequivocal than agriculture-related ones.
14. The distribution of costs in the order water consumer - tax payer - farmer appears acceptable under equity considerations, though it may well be considered a violation of the polluter-pays principle.
15. The main side effects, i.e. income losses of farmers due to nitrate regulations, are compensated for in most cases. Other side effects are not discussed and are not be expected.
16. Substantive or procedural policy innovations have hardly occurred in nitrate policy. The only notable exception perhaps is the massive promotion of the development of denitrification technologies by the responsible ministries in the FRG and the Netherlands which has undoubtedly contributed to a better knowledge about water technological measures.
17. Concerning the politico-economic order, no real violations by nitrate regulations occurred. Restrictions on agricultural practices do not completely fit into the traditional image of the farmer as a free entrepreneur, so that cultural compatibility of agriculture-related nitrate regulations cannot simply be assumed.

In sum, the most important deficiencies in nitrate regulation refer to its cause-orientation, its effectiveness and its efficiency. Judicial and administrative practicability, political viability and societal conformity are fulfilled much better. So, it depends on one's own conception of politics and policy how severe the deficiencies in nitrate regulation must be judged.

If one analyzes the regulatory strategies pursued in an attempt to solve the nitrate problem, according to the substantive-technical, procedural and financial solutions the following pictures emerges (see Figure 6.2). In substance, corrective measures on the water side dominate. Preventive measures on the side of agriculture are only gradually gaining in importance, initially in threatened areas with sandy soils and intensive animal husbandry. This pattern of problem solving is connected with the decreasing competence and power of environmental policy the more it is oriented towards prevention. Thus, cure remains easier than prevention. Political viability and environmental effectiveness tend to run counter to one another. In addition, preventive measures adopted today will normally only contribute to a solution of the nitrate problem tomorrow.

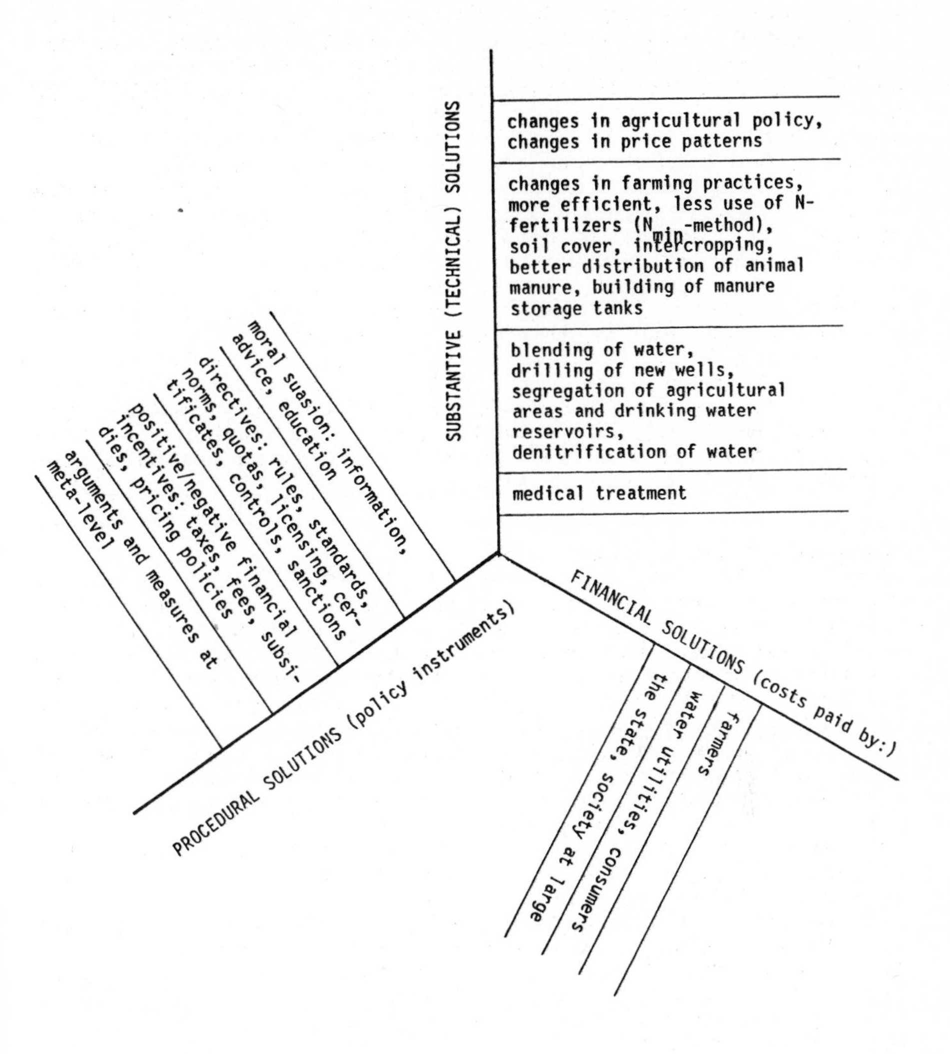

Figure 6.2 Types of regulatory strategies to cope with the nitrate problem in three dimensions

In the past, judical directives and financial incentives have played only a minor role in the regulation of agriculture as far as the nitrate problem is concerned. Partly, such measures as the tax on nitrogen fertilizer and the licensing of fertilization in threatened areas have been explicitly rejected by the responsible administration, for example in the Federal Republic of Germany. Instead, the hope is on moral suasion, mainly from an environmentally-oriented agricultural advisory service, even if the corresponding experiences from the past are disillusioning. This is not to say that environmental counselling in agriculture cannot be successful on a long term basis if it takes into account the cultural adaptation of farmers to local conditions and to larger socio-cultural institutions. While water utilities are obliged to keep to the nitrate standard, the administration is willing to tolerate exceptions for some time and often tend to play down violations.

Concerning cost distributions, water consumers tend to bear the largest share, the federal and state governments, i.e. the taxpayer coming next, with farmers paying least.[1] However, the question is still open as to whether the agricultural lobby will fully succeed in achieving its aims concerning cost distribution.

The role of social subsystems

Modern societies are considerably shaped by different functional social subsystems, such as the science system, the economic system, the political system, etc., which react on ecological demands according to their own codes and programs (Luhmann, 1986). Thus, the politician wants to connect gains in power with environmental engagement, the business company wants to make profits from investments in environmental goods and the scientist wants to get research money and additional reputation for his environmental research. Therefore, it is of some interest to see how different social subsystems have dealt with the nitrate problem, because this may well influence the modes and outcomes of nitrate politics and policy (see Conrad, 1988b).

Scientific experts have played a significant role in the nitrate debate and in nitrate politics. Supported by funds from the political system, science has reacted on the nitrate problem as the first social system and contributed to the development of applicable solutions for the polity, agriculture and water utilities (Conrad, 1988h).

The law system has not yet been strongly involved in the nitrate problem. However, there have been a lot of political actions which are oriented towards legal regulation of nitrate pollution. Therefore, the established judicial routines are crucial for the social treatment of the nitrate problem. Economic aspects are central too; it is not by chance that questions of cost distribution have turned out to be in the focus of nitrate politics. Obviously these economic problems cannot be solved simply by the market mechanism under the dominant legal and institutional conditions, but political decisions and legal prescriptions have always to take economic concerns into account.

The political system has dealt with the nitrate problem primarily *via* symbolic politics and bureaucratic administration. It has been forced to take this problem more serious, but nevertheless nitrate remains but one substance relevant for environmental policy. Political parties have become aware of environmental problems of agriculture in general, but no specific nitrate policy has yet developed with some exception in the Netherlands. Altogether, the resonance of the political system to the nitrate problem has remained a limited one.

The public is less restricted to specific functional reactions to a social problem, and public debate clearly has influenced the evolution of nitrate politics and regulation in general, though mainly at the level of symbolic politics. Environmentalists have had only limited influence in nitrate policy, except in the Netherlands. As long as the nitrate problem is not perceived as one which requires basic reorientations of agriculture, but only better (technical) management, there is no reason for fundamental controversy about the nitrate issue between different social groups. Certainly, however, the varying preferences of attitudes and behaviour versus technical and economic measures, in order to solve the nitrate problem, connects the nitrate debate with general ecological positions.

In sum, the interests and action criteria of the science system and of the major economic subsystems concerned - agriculture and water supply - strongly influence the development of the nitrate debate and politics. Criteria and routines of the political system have then shaped the *specific* features of the societal treatment of the nitrate problem to a large extent. At this general level of description, differences in the role of social subsystems do not matter significantly between the three countries investigated. Again, this situation changes when one takes a closer look at the actual evolution of nitrate debate and policy, as indicated in some of the preceding sections.

Substantive impacts of nitrate policy

In principle, indicators to assess substantive impacts of nitrate policy exist at four levels:[2]

1. decrease of diseases due to nitrate contaminated drinking water,
2. decrease of nitrate concentration in drinking water,
3. decrease of nitrate concentrations in groundwater,
4. decrease of nitrate washout in agriculture.

ad 1:
At the first level, no significant correlations can be expected given our knowledge about existing epidemiological

studies and the lack of any recent case of methaemoglobinaemia being notified. At best, medical studies of babies in families with private wells closed due to high nitrate concentrations could indicate a reduction of the formation of methaemoglobin.

ad 2:
At the second level, successes of nitrate policy are difficult to measure in view of the fact that nitrate levels, on average, are still increasing. However, adherence to the 50 mg/l standard, as far as this can be expected in the coming years, can be attributed to water-related nitrate policy measures.

ad 3:
For groundwater, the problem of the delayed effect exists even more. No areal data are available to investigate this problem.

ad 4:
At the fourth level, one has to make a differentiated assessment. In several demonstration projects nitrate washout was undoubtedly reduced. These results, however, cannot be generalized. So, for the different production spheres of agriculture, only plausible suppositions can be made. The following ones refer to the FRG but would be not very dissimilar for the other two countries.

1. For sugar beet nitrate washout has probably been decreased, but this has little to do with nitrate policy (Feyerabend, 1985).
2. In viticulture, the greening of slopes has expanded and fertilizer dosages have probably been reduced accordingly. This is a concrete success of advisory efforts, but no systematic data on a broad basis are available in this respect.
3. A certain increase in intermediate cropping reduces nitrate washout somewhat and again may be partly due to the agricultural advisory services.
4. Concerning liquid animal manure, there are not sufficient data available to establish whether prohibitions on spreading animal manure in winter has really led to less nitrate washout and not just a shift to other seasons.
5. In vegetable growing, significant changes in fertilizer practices are neither proved nor plausible; they may be expected only in the longer term.
6. For cereals, at best some reduction of uneconomic overfertilization can be assumed. This would keep nitrate washout within acceptable limits under most circumstances, except for many areas in southeast England. Changes in sowing and fertilizer practice have certainly been adopted in eastern England and may well have affected rates of the nitrate leading.[3]
7. For grassland, nitrate washout is small as long as fertilizer rates are well below the Dutch ones. The trans-

formation into arable land with high short-term nitrate washout has been substantially reduced during the last years.
8. In organic farming the nitrate problem has also realized and attempts have been made to improve the situation with respect to organic fertilizers.

In summary, some modest substantive impacts of nitrate policy implementation can be assumed at the level of agricultural nitrate washout and these are probably lowest for Great Britain. These impacts will probably increase somewhat in the future, but this will also depend on the additional (policy) actions undertaken in the years to come.

Overall characteristics of nitrate policy

This section summarizes the main common or diverse features of nitrate policy in the three countries investigated. Due to different spatial compositions of hydrogeological conditions, groundwater extraction and agricultural production patterns, the nitrate problem has a different structure and dimension in each country. With considerable variations in detail, the nitrate debate evolved as primarily a scientific one during the 1970s, and as a more public and political one during the 1980s, triggered by the new nitrate standard in the EC drinking water directive. One may conclude that the nitrate problem gained public significance and political relevance because of the chance occurrence of three or four main influential factors:

1. In recent years a continuous increase of nitrate concentrations in water boreholes was observed by water utilities, mainly in areas of intensive agriculture, which in quite a number of cases led to closure of the wells.
2. Such local events initiated local public debate in some areas. Especially in the FRG and the Netherlands, this was generalized by the media to read, for example, 'agriculture a polluter of groundwater' or 'nitrate a time bomb in other regions too'.
3. Only implementation of the EC drinking water directive of 1980 generated any political necessity for action. At the same time, the conflict of interests between agriculture and water supply became more apparent.
4. The nitrate issue must be seen as part of a growing general agriculture-environment debate which provides a broader perspective and interpretative framework for specific cases and issues, and facilitates their public recognition.

So, there is no special reason why nitrate contamination of ground and drinking water should be at the center of the agriculture-environment debate. It is more by historical coincidence than for systematic reasons that this is so. Predominantly, the nitrate problem is perceived as a controversial issue between farmers and water companies. The involvement of environmental groups and of governmental institutions varies over time and between the three countries. In the UK, quangos (quasi-non-governmental organizations) tend to play a more important role than in the FRG and in the Netherlands. However, informal arrangements and agreements between farmers and water utilities are not to be overlooked there either.

Nitrate policy refers to quite different policy arenas and brought together actors who usually do not interact with each other. The corresponding interaction processes developed relatively reasonably after severe problems in the beginning. It is no wonder, however, that nitrate politics is largely a scape-goat policy game about the costs of solving the nitrate problem where each actor tries to pass the buck. The public or private regulations achieved thus far are hardly the result of a coherent nitrate policy but represent more or less segmented efforts to deal with the problem. Only very recently has the nitrate-related coherence of political action grown, as the Dutch example shows. Non-decisions and delaying decisions have been at least as significant in nitrate policy as (formal) decisions. Agricultural, water and health administrations were, on average, of much greater importance for nitrate politics and policy than political parties and political decision-makers.

The evolution of nitrate policy in the three countries can be fairly well understood as a combined influence. This involved: national policy styles; national, regional and local institutional structures; the pattern of power distribution and interests of the various actors and social institutions involved; the dominant modes of public or private political bargaining processes (the routines of politics); the political will and engagement of individual politicians to effect something concerning the reduction of nitrate pollution. The liquid animal manure ordinance in North Rhine-Westphalia by an environmentally-oriented minister in 1984 and the temporary ban on the establishment and extension of intensive pig and poultry units by the Dutch minister for agriculture in 1984 can be interpreted as examples for this latter determinant of nitrate policy. In the past, nitrate policy essentially remained symbolic (environmental) policy with little substantive impacts. During recent years, this situation is going to change somewhat, more in the Netherlands, less so in Great Britain.[4]

In Table 6.1 the main characteristics of national nitrate policies are evaluated in a heuristic summarizing manner. Finally, three problems of environmental policy are shortly discussed with respect to the evolution of nitrate policy, namely the role of crises, the chances for political steering, and the possibility of separating substantive and distributional conflicts.

Table 6.1
Qualitative comparative evaluation of national nitrate policies

Indicator	Great Britain	West-Germany	Netherlands
nitrate policy existent	hardly	little	partly
perception as a serious problem	low	medium	yes
vested interests	strong	strong	strong
degree of organization and institutionalization of interest in nitrate policy	limited	limited	medium
public pressure in favor of	hardly	varying	considerable
political conflict	yes	yes	yes
conflict potential (strong competing interests)	yes	yes	yes
substantive measures	little, mainly water-related	medium, mainly water-related	medium, water-related, some agricultural-related
policy instruments	primarily moral suasion	moral suasion, directives, some financial incentives	directives, financial incentives, moral suasion
costs to be paid primarily by	water utilities	water utilities, partly farmers, (the state)	water utilities, farmers, (the state)
competences for nitrate policy	central government, bureaucracy and lobbies	mainly state governments	central government
policy implementation	hardly	low	low to medium
degree of pure symbolic nitrate policy	high	high	medium
formality of nitrate policy	low	medium to high	high
policy orientation	(re)distributive	(re)distributive	regulatory
main policy addressees	water supply, agriculture	water supply, agriculture	water supply, agriculture
social and institutional basis	water authorities, environmentalists	water utilities	environmentalists, water utilities, (agricultural board)
priority of agricultural interests	yes	yes	partly
substantive policy impacts	not yet	low	low
time horizon of nitrate policy	10 years	5 - 10 years	15 years

Table 6.1 (continuation)
Qualitative comparative evaluation
of national nitrate policies

Indicator	Great Britain	West-Germany	Netherlands
complexity of nitrate policy	low	medium	medium
detaillation of nitrate policy	low	medium	medium
impacts on agriculture	low	some (manure orders, water protection zones)	some (phosphate fertilizer charges, manure regulation, ban on new farming units)
impacts on water supply	eventually (water protection zones, drinking water standard)	yes (water management law, drinking water ordinance)	yes (nitrate standard, ground protection act)
impacts on the economy in general	no	hardly	low
conflict with the EC and other countries	partly with the EC	some with the EC	no
political viability of the nitrate policy chosen	yes	medium	medium
policy concept	nonpolicy (informal "group" regulation)	legal regulation, conflict avoidance	consensual problem regulation
coherence and consistency of nitrate policy	medium	low to medium	medium
goal attainment (solution of the nitrate problem)	low	low	low
regard of indirect (secondary) impacts	varying	varying	considerable
consideration of functional equivalents	hardly	low	low to medium
accordance of policy orientation and policy means	yes	considerable	considerable
social compatibility	yes	considerable	considerable
effectiveness	no	hardly	hardly
efficiency	low	low	low
equity in cost distrib.	low	low	low to medium
delay of policy impacts	yes	yes	yes
administr. practicability	yes	medium	medium
judicial practicability	yes	mostly	yes
political acceptability of subsidies of violation of the polluter-pays principle	yes	yes	yes
prospects of nitrate policy	ambiguous, will probably develop further	will probably develop further	will continue to develop

Crises are seen by some authors as the mobilizing vehicle to overcome institutional rigidities and political inertia in order to give a more preventive environmental policy a better chance (cf. Jänicke, 1988). In the case of the nitrate problem, it probably goes too far to speak already of a crisis. Only in the Netherlands may connotations of a crisis be inferred from the combination of very intense livestock farming on very sandy soils with groundwater protection objectives beneath. The perception of the severity of this problem has obviously contributed to political action addressing the farmers to an unexpected degree. In view of the many concessions made to agriculture in the new legal provisions, it remains open whether the crisis dimension of the Dutch nitrate problem, in fact, leads to innovative agricultural environmental policy measures with substantive impacts.

Whereas Luhmann (1981) tends to postulate the impossibility of real political steering of social processes in functionally differentiated societies, the actual problem is probably not whether social subsystems can be steered, but the capacity of the political system to steer (Scharpf, 1988). Due to the restraints of democratic politics, the probability is high that strategically reasoning actors tend to exchange more far reaching concessions from the government against short-term compliance in specific topics. One example for this trade off is the acceptance of restrictions on fertilizer use in water protection zones by the farming lobby, which are difficult to control, against the installation of continuous compensation payments. In view of the many interdependencies and even multiple dependencies in modern societies, one possibility of increasing the capacity for political steering may lie in less entanglement and more deployment of different separate but interwoven policies. In principle, it is possible for the state to steer and control nitrate pollution caused by agriculture. However, this may be easier and involve lower political cost if questions of substantive problem solutions and of cost distribution are dealt with in a more separate manner. If questions of agricultural income are dealt with politically in a more explicit and separate manner, farmers - and water utilities, too - will have less chance and less interest in mixing distributive issues with arguments of about the appropriateness of actual agricultural practices *vis-à-vis* nitrate pollution as can be strongly observed at present. The establishment of the water penny in Baden-Württemberg in 1987 could be considered a more prudent environmental policy move on the part of the government had it not been so strongly intermingled with income considerations for the farmers. The political viability of a separate agricultural social policy and an agricultural environmental (nitrate) policy certainly remains an open question, but it may well be worthwhile for environmental policy and for the respective administration to try steps in this direction.

Ecologicalization of agricultural policy?

Ecologicalization, a term translated from German, means the increasing importance and consideration of environmental concerns. Ecologicalization can refer to different levels: ecologicalization of agriculture or of agricultural policy, of environmental consciousness or of environmental action, of different policy fields, different policy levels or different phases of the policy cycle.

It would go beyond the scope of this study even to pinpoint suitable policy measures towards an ecologicalization of agricultural policy (cf. Conrad, 1988b). However, there is a considerable consensus that a certain genuine consideration of environmental concerns in agricultural policy, as well as by the individual farmer, is socially and politically desirable. Consequently, it is worthwhile to try to assess the extent to which the social treatment of nitrate pollution contributes to an ecologicalization of agricultural policy, thereby providing this comparative study with a more far-reaching perspective.

As already stated above, the potential pathfinder role of the nitrate debate for increasing environmental concern in agricultural policy should not be neglected in the Federal Republic of Germany and the Netherlands. Also, experiences with nitrate-related regulations may well extend to future arrangements and approaches in agricultural environmental policy. These experiences indicate, overall, that it is in principle possible to impose environmental regulations on agriculture, but that this is a very difficult, tiresome and lengthy task where the probably price is a deviation from the polluter-pays principle *via* compensation payments for farmers. It is also doubtful if the environment can be protected adequately without rigorous regulations and control (or at least controls on voluntary restrictions) which are compensated for when really severe environmental effects of agriculture are to be addressed such as those resulting from pesticide use or monotonous agricultural landscapes. The emphasis on moral suasion *via* advice on fertilizers and on roundabout ways in nitrate politics have not proven to be successful, effective and efficient approaches up till now. This is not to say that indirect, long-term measures like the internalization of environmental costs with the help of new taxes on agricultural production (Conrad, 1987, 1988f) or supporting changes in taste towards in the general population higher quality food lacking chemical residues as signalled by the expansion of organic farming in recent years, would be superfluous. Again, however, it would be the unescapable pressure from such developments which would silently force farmers to produce in an environmentally more compatible meanner. This might go hand in hand with a change in the corresponding attitudes of many farmers, but this would be a secondary parallel step.

Whether the nitrate problem will be a prototype example of the evolving pattern of an agricultural environmental policy is less likely for Great Britain than for the FRG and the

Netherlands. If it turns out to be one for Great Britain too, this will either signify a lower prevelance of environmental *policy* in the UK, or at least indicate a time lag in the adoption of environmental protection measures in the agricultural sector. In the latter case, this may be considered less serious from a more distant historical perspective in which it matters if environmental protection has got a central social objective in a society, rather than exactly when it occurs.

Whereas a comparison of the specific national characteristics of ecologicalization processes in agricultural policy would require detailed in-depth investigations, it is probably fair to say that the nitrate issue is - to a varying degree - the unintended example of the gradual penetration of West European societies by such processes. Certainly, the legal and institutional constraints and the distribution of power and influence among the political actors usually tend to work to the disadvantage of such a development. In many cases, the unforeseen and unintended side-effects and self-dynamics of certain decisions, such as the EC drinking water directive, may offer a chance to advance the 'ecologicalization' of particular policy issues. Backed by an NO_3 standard of 50 mg/l, actors in favour of an environmentally-sound agriculture may be in a position to work towards a gradual change of the rules of the policy game. This may facilitate the implementation of future environmental policy measures. Substantial success of environmental policy in agriculture, however, seems to require a willingness to put the cost burden on the taxpayer or the consumer. The polluter-pays principle and substantive environmental protection appear to remain rather incompatible in agriculture. Thus, an 'ecologicalization' of agricultural policy which addresses its basic premises and determinants, as demanded by some critics, remains in the distant future.

Notes

1. This statement applies to agriculture as a whole and not to the individual who invests, for example, in building a storage tank for liquid manure.
2. Methodological problems of unequivocal attribution further complicate this assessment but are not considered in detail here.
3. In England, some switching from spring sown cereal crops to autumn sown cereal crops has occurred during the last years.
4. Meanwhile (1988) the situation is about to change significantly in the UK, too.

Bibliography

Aaranovitch, S. (1988), The Nitrates Issue: A Case Study of London, Ms., London.

Baldock, D. (1988), The Nitrates Issue: A Case Study of the Anglian Water Authority, Ms., London.

Bennett, G. (1986), Nitrate Pollution in the Netherlands: Current Situation and Perspectives, Ms., Beek.

Bennett, G. (1987), Environment and Agricultural Policy in the Netherlands, IIUG rep 87-17, Berlin.

BMELF (1988), Agrarbericht 1988, Bonn.

Bruckmeier, K. (1987a), Local Nitrate Policy in West Germany, IIUG dp 87-15, Berlin.

Bruckmeier, K. (1987b), Nitratpolitik vor Ort: Weinbau und Nitratbelastung des Trinkwassers an der Mosel (Landkreis Bernkastel-Wittlich), IIUG rep 87-18, Berlin.

Bruckmeier, K. (1987c), Nitratpolitik vor Ort: Weinbau und Nitratbelastung des Trinkwassers in der Rheinpfalz, IIUG rep 87-19, Berlin.

Bruckmeier, K. (1987d), Nitratpolitik vor Ort: Weinbau und Nitratbelastung des Trinkwassers in Rheinhessen (Landkreis Mainz/Bingen), IIUG rep 87-20, Berlin.

Bruckmeier, K. (1987e), Umweltberatung in der Landwirtschaft, IIUG dp 87-18, Berlin.

Bruckmeier, K. (1988a), Nitratpolitik in der Bundesrepublik Deutschland. Lokale Fallstudien zur Trinkwasser-Nitratbelastung in Gebieten mit intensiver Landwirtschaft, WZB FS II 88-309, Berlin.

Bruckmeier, K. (1988b), The Agriculture Advisory System in Two Countries: A German-British Comparison, Ms., Berlin.

Bruckmeier, K. (1988c), Nitrate Policies in the Federal Republic of Germany, WZB FS II 88-310, Berlin.
Brüggemann, B. et al. (1986), Nitrat im Wasser. Fallstudie Müllheim, Markgräflerland: Zehn Jahre Lernprozeß mit zweifelhaftem Ausgang, IIUG rep 86-12, Berlin.
Bundesministerium für Ernährung, Landwirtschaft und Forsten (BMELF) (ed) (1987), Statistisches Jahrbuch und Ernährung, Landwirtschaft und Forsten in der Bundesrepublik Deutschland 1987, Münster-Hiltrup.
Commission of the European Communities (ed) (1988), The Agricultural Situation in the Community, 1987 Report, Brussels.
Conrad, J. (1984), Increasing Environmental Concern in Agricultural Policy: Nitrate Contamination of Drinking Water - Case Study Federal Republic of Germany, Ms., Berlin.
Conrad, J. (1986), 'Regulation of Agriculturally Induced Nitrate Contamination of Water in some European Countries', in V. de Kosinsky and M. de Somer (eds), Water Resources for Rural Areas and their Comunities, Proceedings, vol. 3, Gent (IIUG pre 85-16, Berlin).
Conrad, J. (1987), Alternative Uses for Land and the New Farmworker: Segregation versus Integration, IIUG rep 87-1, Berlin (FAST Occasional Paper 179, Brüssel).
Conrad, J. (1988a), Nitrate Debate and Nitrate Policy in FR Germany, Land Use Policy, vol. 5, p. 207 (IIUG pre 87-8, Berlin).
Conrad, J. (1988b), Nitratdiskussion und -politik in der Bundesrepublik Deutschland, Ms., Berlin.
Conrad, J. (1988c), Nitrate Pollution and Politics in West Germany, Ms., Berlin.
Conrad, J. (ed) (1988d), Wassergefährdung durch die Landwirtschaft, Berlin.
Conrad, J. (1988e), 'Zur Neuorientierung der Agrarpolitik. Vergleichende Evaluation agrarpolitischer Konzepte', in W. Henrichsmeyer and C. Langbehn (eds), Wirtschaftliche und soziale Auswirkungen unterschiedlicher agrarpolitischer Konzepte, Münster-Hiltrup (IIUG pre 87-10, Berlin).
Conrad, J. (1988f), 'Agrarumweltpolitik durch Politikentflechtung: Chancen und Risiken', in U.E. Simonis (ed), Lernen von der Umwelt - Lernen für die Umwelt, Berlin.
Conrad, J. (1988g), 'Präventive Umweltpolitik im Agrarsektor: Optionen und Restriktionen', in U.E. Simonis (ed), Präventive Umweltpolitik, Frankfurt a.M. (IIUG pre 87-2, Berlin).
Conrad, J. (1988h), Die Rolle wissenschaftlicher Expertise in der Agrar-Umwelt-Debatte am Beispiel des Nitratproblems, Ms., Berlin.
Conrad, J. and Knoepfel, P. (1984), Increasing Environmental Concern in Agricultural Policy. An International Comparative Study of Political Processes Relating to Agrochemicals, Agriculture and Food: Nitrate Contamination of Drinking Water, Ms., Berlin, Lausanne.
Conrad, J. and Uka, W. (1987), Die Agrarsubventionen der Europäischen Gemeinschaft. Daten, Fakten, Trends, IIUG rep 87-7, Berlin.

Conrad, J. and Teherani-Krönner, P. (1989), 'The Politics of Shit: Regulation of Liquid Manure Application in North Rhine-Westphalia and Lower Saxony', *Policy and Politics*, vol. 17.

Department of Environment (1983), *Agriculture and Pollution* (The Government's Response to the Seventh Report of the Royal Commission), HMSO, London.

Department of Environment (1986), *Nitrate in Water* (A Report of the Nitrate Coordination Group), HMSO, London.

Deutsche Forschungsgemeinschaft (DFG) (ed) (1982), *Nitrat-Nitrit-Nitrosamine in Gewässern*, Weinheim.

Deutscher Verein des Gas- und Wasserfaches (DVGW) (ed) (1987), *European Conference. Impact of Agriculture on Water Resources - Consequences and Perspectives*, Eschborn.

Dudley, N. (1986), *Nitrates in Food and Water*, London Food Commission, London.

Easton, D. (1965), *A Systems Analysis of Political Life*, New York.

EUREAU (1987), *The Nitrate Problem: Declaration by Eureau on Solving the Nitrate Problem*, Brussels.

European Commission (1980), *Official Journal of the EEC Commission L 229* (EC Drinking Water Directive), Brussels.

Feyerabend, I. (1985), *Zuckerproduktion und Stickstoffdüngung. Umweltschutz als Nebeneffekt*, IIUG rep 85-3, Berlin.

Finck, H.F. and Haase, K. (1987), 'Nitratbelastung des Grundwassers - ökonomische Beurteilung von Alternativen', *Angewandte Wissenschaft*, vol. 347, Münster-Hiltrup.

Friends of the Earth (1986), *Nitrate: Boon or Bane*.

Gitay, H. and Wathern, P. (1988), *Environmental Advisory Services in UK Agriculture*, Ms., Aberysthwyth.

Gitschel, M. (1987a), *Nitratpolitik vor Ort: Intensive Landwirtschaft und Trinkwasserversorgung im Kreis Viersen*, IIUG rep 87-11, Berlin.

Gitschel, M. (1987b), *Nitratpolitik vor Ort: Gemüseanbau und Grundwassernutzung im Hessischen Ried*, IIUG rep 87-14, Berlin.

Hafenecker, P. (1989), *Nitratpolitik vor Ort: Augsburg als Modell?* Ms., Berlin.

Hill, M. (1988), *Nitrate Policy in Britain*, Ms., Newcastle.

Hill, M. et al. (1988), *Non-decision-Making in Pollution Control in Britain: Nitrate Pollution, the EEC Drinking Water Directive and Agriculture*, Ms., Newcastle.

House of Commons Environment Committee (1987), *Pollution of Rivers and Estuaries*, HMSO, London.

Hünermann, G. (1987), *Nitratpolitik vor Ort: Trinkwasserbelastung im Raum Nortorf (Kreis Rendsburg-Eckernförde)*, IIUG rep 87-21, Berlin.

Hünermann, G. et al. (1987), *Nitratforschung in der Bundesrepublik Deutschland in den 80er Jahren*, IIUG rep 87-12, Berlin.

ICI (1986), *Nitrate and our Environment*, London.

Jänicke, M. (1988), 'Ökologische Modernisierung. Optionen und Restriktionen präventiver Umweltpolitik', in U.E. Simonis (ed), *Präventive Umweltpolitik*, Frankfurt a.M.

van der Kley, L. and Bennett, G. (1988), Nitrate Policy in the Netherlands, WZB FS II 88-306, Berlin.
Knoepfel, P. and Zimmermann, W. (1987), Ökologisierung von Landwirtschaft, Frankfurt a.M.
Kommission der Europäischen Gemeinschaft (1983 ff.), Die Lage der Landwirtschaft. Bericht 1982 ff., Brussels.
Kromarek, P. (1986), Die Trinkwasserrichtlinie der EG und die Nitratwerte, IIUG rep 86-9, Berlin.
Länderarbeitsgemeinschaft Wasser (LAWA) (1987), LAWA-Grundwasserschutzprogramm 1987, Berlin.
Larrue, C. and Knoepfel, P. (1988), La pollution par les nitrates: Pratiques et politiques des paysans, des administrateurs et des producteurs d'engrais, Ms., Créteil.
Luhmann, N. (1981), Politische Theorie im Wohlfahrtsstaat, München.
Luhmann, N. (1986), Ökologische Kommunikation, Opladen.
Matthews, A. and Trede, K.-J. (1983), Agrarpolitik und Agrarsektor im Vereinigten Königreich, Kiel.
Ministerie L&V (1986), Meststoffenwet, Staatsblad 598, Staatsuitgeverij, Den Haag.
Ministerie L&V (1987), Mestactieprogramma, Kamerstuk 882, Staatsuitgeverij, Den Haag.
Ministry of Agriculture, Fisheries and Food/Welsh Office (1985), Code of Good Agricultural Practice.
National Academy of Sciences (NAS) (1981), The Health Effects of Nitrate, Nitrite and N-Nitroso Compounds, Washington D.C.
Obermann, P. (1984), 'Möglichkeiten des Nitratabbaus im Sicker- und Grundwasser', Gewässerschutz - Wasser - Abwasser, vol. 65, p. 577.
de Potter, H. (1986), Nitraat in Nederland, Stichting Natuur en Milieu, Utrecht.
Rohmann, U. and Sontheimer, H. (1985), Nitrat im Grundwasser, Ursachen, Bedeutung, Lösungswege, Karlsruhe.
Royal Commission on Environmental Pollution (1979), Seventh Report: Agriculture and Pollution, HMSO, London.
Royal Society (1983), The Nitrogen Cycle of the United Kingdom, London.
Scharpf, W. (1988), 'Verhandlungssysteme, Verteilungskonflikte und Pathologien der politischen Steuerung', in: M.G. Schmidt (ed), Staatstätigkeit, PVS Sonderheft 19/88, Opladen.
Schmidt, M.G. (ed) (1988), Staatstätigkeit. Internationale und historisch vergleichende Analysen, PVS Sonderheft 19/88, Opladen.
Rat von Sachverständigen für Umweltfragen (SRU) (1985), Umweltprobleme in der Landwirtschaft, Stuttgart.
Standing Technical Advisory Committee on Water Quality (1981), Fourth Biennial Report 1981-3, HMSO, London.
Stiftung Warentest (1988), 'Vom Acker in die Leitung. Nitrat im Trinkwasser', Test, no. 10.
Teherani-Krönner, P. (1985), Tauziehen um eine agrarumweltpolitische Regulierung. Die Gülleverordnung von Nordrhein-Westfalen, IIUG rep 85-8, Berlin.

Teherani-Krönner, P. (1987), Implementation der Gülleverordnung in Nordrhein-Westfalen, IIUG rep 87-4, Berlin.

Teherani-Krönner, P. (1988a), Nitratpolitik vor Ort: Wohin mit den Gülleüberschüssen aus Vechta?, WZB FS II 88-305, Berlin.

Teherani-Krönner, P. (1988b), Nitratpolitik im Landkreis Osnabrück: So ernst war der Gülleerlaß nicht gemeint!, Ms., Berlin.

Teherani-Krönner, P. (1988c), Nitratpolitik vor Ort: Gülleregulierung und Wasserpolitik im Kreis Borken, Ms., Berlin.

Teherani-Krönner, P. (1988d), Nitratpolitik vor Ort: Brunnenschließung in Minden-Lübbecke, Ms., Berlin.

Trede, K.-J. (1983), Agrarpolitik und Agrarsektor in den Niederlanden, Kiel.

Trede, K.-J. and Filter, W. (1983), Agrarpolitik und Agrarsektor in der Bundesrepublik Deutschland, Kiel.

Uka, W. (1989), Nitratpolitik vor Ort: Eskalierende Grundwasserprobleme im Raum Heidelberg, Ms., Berlin.

VDLUFA (ed) (1985), Nitrat, Frankfurt a.M.

Vetter, H. (1985), 'Lösung des Nitratproblems - Was kann die Landwirtschaft tun?', Agrar-Europa, vol. 5, Sonderbeilage 1.

Wathern, P. (1988a), Agriculture and Surface Water Quality Problems in England and Wales. An Overview and Local Cases, Ms., Aberystwyth.

Wathern, P. (1988b), Nitrate and Drinking Water in the Yorkshire Water Authority Area, Ms., Aberysthwyth.

Wathern, P. and Baldock, D. (1987), Regulating the Interface between Agriculture and the Environment in the United Kingdom, IIUG rep 87-15, Berlin.

Werkgroep Nitraatuitspoeling in waterwingebieden (1985), Nitraatproblematiek bij grondwaterwinning in Nederland, ICW rapport 12, Wageningen.

WHO (1984), Guidelines for Drinking Water Quality, Geneva.